RESPECT FOR THE EARTH

RESPECT FOR THE EARTH

SUSTAINABLE DEVELOPMENT

Chris Patten • Tom Lovejoy • John Browne •
Gro Brundtland • Vandana Shiva
and HRH The Prince of Wales

PROFILE BOOKS

THE BBC IN ASSOCIATION WITH PROFILE BOOKS LTD

First published in 2000 by
Profile Books Ltd
58A Hatton Garden
London EC1N 8LX
www.profilebooks.co.uk

Typeset in Bembo by
MacGuru
info@macguru.org.uk
Printed and bound in Great Britain by
Biddles Ltd, Guildford and King's Lynn

A CIP catalogue record for this book is available from the British Library.

ISBN 1 86197 254 7

Contents

The Contributors   vi

Introduction – Jonathon Porritt   ix

1 Governance – Chris Patten   1

2 Biodiversity – Tom Lovejoy   22

3 Business – John Browne   36

4 Health and Population –
   Gro Harlem Brundtland   49

5 Poverty and Globalisation – Vandana Shiva   64

6 A Royal View – HRH The Prince of Wales   80

   Conclusion   90

   The Public Debate   114

THE CONTRIBUTORS

In a change to tradition, the 2000 BBC Lectures had one theme – sustainable development – but were delivered by five different thinkers, each eminent in a different field. At the end of the run, the Prince of Wales presented his own views on the topic in a round-table discussion with all five lecturers.

Chris Patten is now Commissioner for External Relations for the European Union. He was UK Minister for Overseas Development, and the last Governor of Hong Kong. When he was Secretary of State for the Environment he was responsible for the UK's first White Paper on sustainable development, *Our Common Inheritance* (1990). He is the author of *East and West* (Macmillan, 1998).

Dr Tom Lovejoy is Chief Biodiversity Advisor for the World Bank and Counsellor at the Smithsonian Institution, Washington. He specialises in the environmental biology of the tropics and Latin America. He co-edited *Global Warming And Biological Diversity* (Yale University Press, 1992). Championing biodiversity in all areas, he was also a founder of the American public television series, Nature.

Sir John Browne is Chief Executive Officer of BP Amoco, which is Britain's largest company and the third largest oil corporation in the world. He read Physics at St John's College, Cambridge, and graduated from Stanford Business School. Sir John is a non-executive director of some other companies, including SmithKline Beecham and Intel.

Dr Gro Harlem Brundtland is Director General of the World Health Organisation. She started her career as a doctor, specialising in child-care and public health. She was Minister of the Environment and Prime Minister of Norway. In her report to the World Commission on Environment and Development (which led to the United Nations Earth Summit in Rio de Janeiro in 1992) she baldly stated that if we do not change our ways, we risk our own extinction. She has done much to increase global ecological awareness.

Dr Vandana Shiva is Founder Director of the Research Foundation for Science, Technology and

Ecology in New Delhi. She trained as a physicist and advises a number of governments on global issues. She is an active leading member of many NGOs; the author of *Biopiracy* (1997); and founder of Navdanya, an Indian national movement to promote the diversity and use of native seeds.

The Prince of Wales has been airing his concerns about environmental matters for many years (long before ecological awareness became mainstream). He actively supports sustainable development in his speeches; in his support for various 'green' organisations; and in his own commitment to organic farming at Highgrove.

Introduction

All species have a deep survival instinct. They do everything they can to secure their own survival chances. And that is as true of humans as it is of the Siberian tiger or the lowliest of bacteria. We humans even have a name for our survival instinct: it's called 'sustainable development'. Which means, quite simply, living on this planet as if we intended to go on living here for ever.

It was only about thirty years ago that it started to dawn on people that our survival instinct had somehow got buried in the pursuit of ever-greater material prosperity. To generate that prosperity we were literally laying waste to the planet, tearing down forests, damming rivers, polluting the air, eroding top soil, warming the atmosphere, depleting fish stocks and covering everything with concrete and tarmac.

Even then, experts like Thomas Lovejoy were warning of the impact of all this on other creatures – or biological diversity, as the jargon now has it. The United Nations Environment Programme has calculated that today's rate of extinction is running at more than 10,000 times what it would naturally be without the impact of the human species. And as our numbers grow, by an additional 85 million or so a year, the pressures on the planet and its life-support systems (on which all species depend, including ourselves) continue to mount year by year.

To start with, most politicians and business people dismissed these warnings as the overheated scaremongering of 'weird and wacky' environmentalists. But the scientific evidence kept on getting stronger, and in 1987 a group of leading experts under the chairmanship of Gro Harlem Brundtland produced a report (*Our Common Future*) which said quite simply that we had no option but to change our ways or ultimately risk our own extinction.

And the only alternative to the prevailing model of economic growth that takes no account of either poorer people or the planet was sustainable development: 'development that meets the needs of the present without compromising the ability of future generations to meet their own needs.'

This was the first time the social aspect of sustainable development was given such prominence. Poverty is one of the greatest drivers of environmental destruction, and for development to be truly sustainable we have to address ourselves as much to poverty alleviation, education and better healthcare for all as we do to climate change and toxic pollution. This message was power-fully reinforced by the 1992 Earth Summit, the greatest ever gathering of world leaders, which unambiguously reasserted both the unsustainability of our current model of progress and the pressing need for a sustainable alternative.

Nearly ten years on, it has to be said that progress has been pretty slow. True enough, sustainable develop-ment is hardly the sexiest of concepts to drive the required transformation in our societies and economies. And there are still so many misunderstandings about what it really means.

It doesn't require, for instance, an end to economic growth as some have argued, but rather the kind of eco-nomic growth that is environmentally sustainable (meaning it doesn't go on eroding those critical life sup-port systems) and socially equitable. As John Browne (the Chief Executive of BP Amoco) points out, this represents a huge challenge to all industries but it also offers huge opportunities. Only recently has it become clear to the business community that looking after the environment is completely compatible with looking after shareholders. The notion of eco-efficiency (reduc-ing costs by eliminating waste and pollution and max-imising resource efficiency) underpins this business case for sustainable development.

However, far too few big companies have really seized hold of this challenge. What's more, as critics like

Vandana Shiva cogently argue, the same companies are the principal drivers of a process of economic globalisation that may be accelerating environmental destruction and further widening the gap between rich and poor.

For governments around the world, sustainable development is proving a tough nut to crack. After 250 years or so promising people more and more through permanent economic expansion, it requires real political leadership to start shifting the emphasis onto quality of life and a more balanced and sustainable pattern of economic development. Such changes can only be brought about by consent, not by political diktat. Chris Patten was one of the first politicians in the UK to address this democratic challenge as the Secretary of State for the Environment responsible for the UK's first White Paper on sustainable development, *Our Common Inheritance*, in 1990.

The scale of the challenge is daunting. But as all this year's Reith lecturers point out, things are now moving in the right direction, albeit too slowly and too patchily.

But sustainable development is not a single issue, like the 'environment' or 'world trade'. It is essentially a different model of progress, balancing the social and economic needs of the human species with the non-negotiable imperative of living within Planet Earth's natural limits. His Royal Highness, The Prince of Wales has been at the forefront of the debate on sustainable development for many years. For him, and for others, it is as much a challenge to our philosophy and personal values as to our political and economic systems, requiring as it does a dramatic shift from an ethos of exploitation and domination to one of stewardship and global responsibility.

Jonathon Porritt has been one of the most influential advocates on behalf of the environment over the past twenty-five years. He is Programme Director of the Forum for the Future. He has been closely involved with The Prince of Wales's Business and Environment Programme.

I

Governance

Chris Patten

I sometimes think that I have done my full ration of school speech days. The one that I remember most clearly – etched in my memory so that its vivid images return to trouble me again and again – provides a bleak paradigm for this lecture.

At the time, I was Britain's Overseas Development Minister, distributor-in-chief of inadequate supplies of Band-Aid to the world's wounded. In the course of my duties, I was in Ethiopia – yet again – but this time to visit the refugees from another country's calamities. There was a savage war between the Islamic north of Sudan and the Christian south. (Twelve years later the war grinds bloodily on.) I was sent to visit the refugee camps established for the Sudanese victims of the war just over the border in Ethiopia. A haven in Ethiopia. The mind boggled.

We flew down – the ambassador, my staff, the man from the British Council and me – from Addis Ababa to the border in a government plane. A couple of weeks later the same plane on the same journey crashed, killing a distinguished American congressman and the rest of the passengers.

We inspected the camp on a sweltering morning. We were hot, wet and increasingly dark with despair at the sheer misery we witnessed and the implacable evil that had caused it. Most of the refugees were young and male. They had fled their homes and villages, fearing genocidal slaughter, trekking for weeks across a blasted landscape to find relief on the far edge of the Nile flood plain. I asked one little boy how he and his friends – only half of whom had survived the journey – had found their way to safety. 'It was simple', he replied, 'we followed the bodies'. So they had plotted a path from corpse to corpse through the equatorial wilderness and, safely arrived, the first thing they did was to establish a school. There were about 12,000 pupils waiting for us and they were drawn up in a great circle on the baked mud in the middle of their huts to hear a few words of encouragement from the visiting white minister.

The man from the British Council, that insanely

undervalued institution, had demonstrated its worth once again by bringing some footballs that served more purpose than my little homily about the importance of education for a happier future. The self-appointed headmaster, a Protestant pastor, asked if they could all sing for us. We stood there, the sweat dribbling down our red faces, as they sang the Lord's Prayer in their native language, Dinka or Nuer I think. And then I was told they wanted to sing a text from Isaiah. Feet stamping, hands clapping, they chanted the verses. At the time I assumed they were singing about beating swords into ploughshares, but back in the ambassador's bungalow on the hillside above Addis Ababa I thumbed curiously through the Gideon Bible in my bedroom, the fan spinning overhead, to confirm my suspicion. I was wrong. They'd sung Isaiah 9:2, 'The people that walked in darkness have seen a great light: they that dwell in the land of the shadow of death, upon them hath the light shined.'

Those thousands of kids had certainly lived in the land of the shadow of death, young citizens of that clutch of ill-fated countries blighted by war, by political breakdown, by environmental disaster and (in a sense) by geography. As David Landes, the author of *The Wealth and Poverty of Nations* argues, 'geography ... brings bad tidings', in this case that to live in that tropical or semi-tropical zone between the Tropics of Cancer and Capricorn – its extreme heat helping to multiply the insects and parasites that sicken and kill – is to struggle against loaded dice. Yet as Landes also argues, no one should regard geography as destiny. We can promote development and even sustain it in the most unpromising conditions if we have the will, if we see the light, if we embrace and abide by a value system both as simple as the words of Isaiah and as richly complex as the inter-connections of our ecological system. It is of course equally true that we can mess up the management of the more favoured zones of our planet if we are sufficiently careless or if public policy and the institutions and values that should sustain it are warped or plain wrong.

'Sustainable development' is a phrase first coined by the United Nations Conference on the Human Environment – the Stockholm Conference – in 1972. Fifteen years later the Brundtland Commission on Environment and Development defined it thus, 'to meet the needs of the present without compromising the ability of future generations to meet their own needs'. I have a friend who puts it rather more simply. 'We should live here on earth', he says, 'as though we were intending to stay for good, not just visit for the weekend'.

Most governments these days – the good, the bad and even the ugly – have an Environment Department and an Environment Minister charged with implementing Brundtland. I did the job once myself, sitting at the top of one of the most unattractive buildings in London trying to make Britain a little greener, drafting the first comprehensive White Paper on the subject, negotiating a toughening of the international agreement on halons and chloro-fluorocarbons, trying to reverse (a cyclical struggle this) the attempt to cover England's southern shires with new housing estates and shopping malls. There was more to it than that, probably more than there had been before and certainly less than there should have been, but it all felt a little like 'finger in the dyke' stuff.

We understand today that sustainable development is about much more than environment policy defined in terms of departments, ministers and white papers. It requires a mosaic of institutions, policies and values. Mosaic may even be too static a word for what is required; it is really a political ecosystem that is needed to save the real one.

Take what has too often happened in some of those countries disadvantaged by geography where environmental blight has frequently had the most immediately calamitous consequences for whole populations. The historical pattern is less unusual than we would like. For example about forty years ago, country X gained its independence, after a century of colonial rule that few today would attempt to justify. It inherited, probably fought for, a model pluralist constitution. There was a bicameral parliament fairly elected. There were independent courts. There was a free press. Civil liberties were constitutionally guaranteed. 'Habeas corpus' defended the individual. A small army was under the control of the civil authorities. The elected president was in the former governor's mansion; the military were in their barracks; beans, maize and pulses were cropped; mineral resources were mined from the rock; God was in heaven.

Then the president began to stir uneasily under the restraints of constitutionalism, or maybe he was replaced by a Sandhurst socialist who had not himself read Jennings on the British Constitution but knew someone who claimed to have read Tawney. Political opposition was curtailed. The press was muzzled. Unchecked, political leaders ceased to make any distinction between the state's reserves and their own bank accounts. Family values came to mean the president's family skimming the nation's GDP. The first victim was usually the independence of the courts, and with that gone the integrity of the public services disappeared too. In order to hold onto power the army was cosseted, but spending money on the military meant there was less for educating children or agricultural extension or for primary healthcare. Soldiers were paid; teachers and nurses were not. Taxes on the honestly entrepreneurial were hiked. Ethnic minorities were dispossessed. Industries were nationalised, which often resulted in their assets being slipped into back pockets.

To retain popularity or at least acquiescence in urban areas, food prices were held down, which discouraged farmers, already often discriminated against by global trading rules, from growing as much as they could have done. Increasing rural poverty led to deforestation and the collapse of rural infrastructure, for example irrigation systems. As the mountains were stripped of their trees, so the rain gouged the soil from the rock, silted the rivers and flooded the plains. It was an awful cycle of political repression, war, corruption, woeful economic management, environmental calamity, starvation and debt.

I retain several images of the process. The brand-new high-tech hospital in east Africa, with no money or skill to repair the equipment, no doctors to provide treatment (having been trained, they'd emigrated to earn more money in America and Europe), no money for food, no drugs for the patients. Meanwhile in the surrounding countryside, illness and disease caused by iron deficiency laid the population low.

The power station built by aid donors as much to preserve a part of British industry as to deliver power to consumers who, from the Finance Ministry down, declined to pay for it. The factories full of clapped-out equipment. The dams un-repaired. The sand advancing year by year into the once arable land. The military dictator explained a fine point about economic policy and the environment: 'As I said to my late predecessor,' he began. He had hanged his 'late predecessor'. And everywhere, everywhere, the clapped-out Land Rovers.

What does a motor vehicle have to do with sustainable development and good governance? Simple. The Land Rover is the heroic warhorse of development policy. As a donor of aid we had given fleets of those splendid vehicles to poor countries. And everywhere you went there were the same fleets of them, broken down, rusting in the rain and the sun. We began projects to repair them and put them back on the road – good projects. And would there today be enough money for the ministry to pay for their petrol? Would there be a trained local mechanic to drop the sump? Would there be the basic elements of public administration to keep the vehicles on the road – or dust tracks more like? What about a few bicycles instead? For me, there is an umbilical link between Land Rovers, 'habeas corpus', wooded mountain sides, prosperous farmers, the ballot box, freedom of speech and improving your own quality of life without wrecking the prospects for your children. It's a connection between spiritual, political and environmental pollution, a point made by Vaclav Havel about the consequences for Central and Eastern Europe of communist tyranny there.

That should remind us that we are not talking about problems and connections that only affect developing countries. Look at the environmental deterioration of parts of our own continent under so-called people's democracies. And note that sustainable development is challenged even by the practices of liberal, pluralist democracies. Concepts of good governance or democracy were arguably implicit in the earliest definitions of sustainable development. In recent years, the references have been explicit. The richer countries club, the OECD, is today seeking ways in which developing countries can be helped to promote democratisation, civil society and the rule of law and to conform to internationally accepted human rights norms.

The first, widely accepted hallmark of good, efficient government is that it should be accountable, that those it serves should be able to question what it is doing and change what it is doing. Some regard this as a recipe for inconsistency and mess. By and large, that was the attitude of Asian authoritarians to the idea of accountability and public participation in government. Who could know better than them what was good for their people? That argument took a tumble with the '97 crash. You usually make better policy if it has to be justified in the cut and thrust of open debate. If you are going to be held to account for what you are doing, you are more likely to think it through rather carefully.

Accountable government gains legitimate public authority, a vital quality when unpopular decisions have to be taken or good policies have to be enforced. We should remember that good government is not ineffectual government. It has to be able to carry through what it wishes to do even when this is unpopular. Good government will always operate within a framework of laws that entrench rights and ensure predictability and fairness in dealings between individual citizens, between individual companies or between citizens and companies on the one hand and the institutions of the state on the other. One of the most difficult things for politicians of an authoritarian bent to comprehend is that the law is master of government and governed alike; it is the guarantor of liberty. Remember the exchange between Thomas More and young William Roper in Robert Bolt's *A Man for all Seasons*:

'What would you do?' asks More of Roper, who yearns to battle evil.

'Cut a great road through the law to get after the Devil?'

Roper replies, 'I'd cut every law in England to do that!'

Thomas More retorts, 'And when the last law was down, and the Devil turned on you – where would you hide Roper, the laws all being flat?'

Democracies are not corruption-free zones, either in business or public administration. Yet the scale of corruption and its corrosive impact on sustainable development is limited by democratic practice and a free judiciary. In an open, plural society even where there is still no cultural recognition of the primacy of public responsibility over private gain, corrupt practices will nevertheless have to run the gauntlet of relentless criticism and exposure by parliament, press and courts.

Freedom of speech and government transparency help secure at least the rudiments of public well-being. Amartya Sen has argued convincingly that famines do not happen in open, independent societies. The famine that overwhelmed Mao's China in the 1950s could not have happened in Nehru's India. It was no coincidence that the devastating forest fires that blackened Asia's skies in 1997 were accompanied by media clampdowns in Indonesia and Malaysia. You might cough and splutter; you might not see the sun for weeks except through a thick haze; but from Kuala Lumpur to Jakarta, you were not allowed to draw public attention to the effect of slash-and-burn policies in Java's tropical forests. If you were not allowed to read about it in the newspapers, it could not be happening. There was a ghastly symmetry between Asia's environmental disaster of 1997 and its financial crash of the same year. In both cases, cover-up, secretiveness and a state of self-deluding denial produced disaster, with the ignorant greed of western commercial and political interests frequently conniving at the catastrophe.

No hymn to democracy can be without its qualifying verses. After all, as Jane Jacobs reminds us, everything is disappointing in practice. Democracy is not the only ingredient of good governance, nor a guarantee that those who are bound by its disciplines and espouse its philosophy will look after the world with all due care and attention. Democracy is more likely to produce better government on the side of sustainable development. But to borrow the song title, 'It ain't necessarily so'.

Dictators are rarely friends of the earth. But even those democratic leaders who espouse environmentalism sometimes appear fatally constrained by a prevailing public mood or a powerful private lobby. In some cultural manifestations of environmental concern, the United States leads the world. Yet its contribution to the global struggle against climate change is hamstrung by the seeming political imperative of keeping energy prices low.

Some concede that democracy may be the most sustainable form of government, not least because it contains self-correcting mechanisms, and that it may be the least worst way of protecting the environment. But they question whether even at its most sophisticated we can really depend on it to take uncomfortable decisions for the unverifiable benefit of future generations. The question is in a sense unanswerable. But I can't think of any sort of government likely to be better placed to take on and win this sort of argument, for example, by seeking better ways of costing the environmental results, of our daily choices and trying to incorporate them into political and economic decisions.

We can look for another potential source of democratic strength by considering one of its imperfections, the tendency from time to time for democracy to turn into illiberal majoritarianism. The ballot box is only the mechanism of democracy. A liberal democracy requires more than elections. It needs an environment of checks and balances, of accommodating not exclusive values, that enables it to flourish in the interests of all its citizens and not merely in the interest of the largest number of them. Part of this essential fabric of a liberal democracy is what we today call civil society, or – to use the buzz word – the 'social capital' of a community: the independent groupings and bodies from professions and churches to non-governmental organisations. Their role and influence have been massively increased as fast as those of national elected governments have been reduced. Where democratic governments fail, civil society – non-governmental organisations – can come to the rescue, ensuring that its own agenda prevails or at least is given greater heed. And this is specially relevant to the area we are discussing, since democratic governments have not always been conspicuously good at meeting their environmental responsibilities. So to secure sustainable development, it is suggested that traditional notions of good governance must take far greater account of civil society.

'To be attached to the subdivision', Edmund Burke wrote, 'to love the little platoon we belong to in society, is the first principle (the germ as it were) of public affections'. All politics is local. We identify with family, club, church, village, town, interest group as well as country. These loyalties always formed the underpinnings of democratic society, and sensible governments recognised this. But social, economic and technological changes have meant that today the exercise of loyalty to the 'little platoons' can compromise and undermine the authority of the traditional mechanisms for delivering even sensitive and sensible majoritarian government.

First, democratic governments have been based traditionally on strong, competing mass parties. In almost every country, mass parties are a thing of the past. They wither on the electoral vine. They are in part the victims of an end to Manichaean politics – good versus evil, state versus individual, Left versus Right. There is still a Left and there is still a Right, but the zealotry and heresies have largely passed into history as most politics huddles around a centrist agenda based on the triumph of market liberalism with as much of a human face as finance ministers and banks will allow. Social change has blurred the old distinctions of lifestyle, housing and employment that also sustained political parties. Everywhere, the problem of financing crumbling political organisations threatens to put them in hock to the rich with opinions or to interest groups with their own focused ambitions. Everywhere, there is the danger of takeover by well-organised minorities. Everywhere, more people join organisations that wish to protect birds, clean up the air, ban road building and save the planet than join those that want to save the inheritance of Churchill or Attlee, Roosevelt or Eisenhower.

Second, national democratic governments themselves are squeezed from above and below. As technology and trade break down barriers, so governments have to cope with the commercial clout of multinational corporations. I do not myself see cloven hooves under every boardroom table; corporations can be good, bad or indifferent. What is more, their power is not new. But it seems unarguable that they are more powerful today than ever before. It is easy to see the giants of information technology both cutting governments down to size and giving individuals and the 'little platoons' much more power. There was a story in the *Washington Post* a few weeks ago asserting that Microsoft, which had been locked in courtroom battles with the US Justice Department, was funding lobbyists to secure cuts in that department's budget. At the same time miniaturisation of electronics and the spread – courtesy of Microsoft among others – of knowledge and information at a pace and in quantities never before imagined, limit the ability of national governments to exercise their traditional authority, not least that based on the claim of superior intelligence. The Internet is a great leveller.

Third, governments and multinational enterprises are smart enough to know that the pooling of national sovereignty is required in some areas where national boundaries have been overrun by economics, environmental change and technology. International organisations – on a regional or global scale – have been created to try to manage the consequences of globalisation. But they have difficulty attracting the public loyalty required to give them the legitimacy they require; and they also lack the public approbation gained by a sense of participation in decision-making and of openness to public accounting. That is a problem even for the institutions of a regional organisation like the European Union that has elaborate structures of democratic oversight. It is a far greater problem for global bodies like the World Trade Organisation, the International Monetary Fund and the World Bank.

Into the gaps, the crevices, the nooks and crannies, floods a tide of pressure group and NGO activity, and this is in many respects admirable, a welcome demonstration of growing global pluralism. The cutting edge of all this civil society activism has been environmental, the campaign in various ways to save what is thought essential for sustainable development. But I find myself asking the awkward question – is it actually very sustainable given that it isn't obviously democratic? Do we not face the danger of discrediting good arguments by pursuing them in a manner that threatens us all with something even worse than majoritarianism, namely minoritarianism? Now I should make a distinction here between NGOs in developed countries and many of those in countries that are still developing. There, NGOs are sometimes more democratic than the structures of government. They struggle bravely for democracy itself. But that is not the case in the richer north of the globe.

So with that caveat, let us take a particular and rather controversial example of potential minoritarianism. We have witnessed recently growing signs of pressure group and NGO activity at meetings of international organisations. Many think that the high point so far was the lobbying and street parades during the Seattle meetings of the WTO. You remember the TV pictures. My own favourite showed a lobbyist, a foot soldier in civil society's growing regiment of 'little platoons', carrying a banner on which was written, 'The World Wide Movement Against Globalisation'. There will be more of all this at the spring meetings this year of the World Bank and the International Monetary Fund. But is the demonisation of global trade and technological progress good for sustainable development and how democratic is it? Globalisation is not new. Look a hundred years ago at the pattern of trade, overseas investment and immigration. That was globalisation without today's technology. What makes things different today is that the triumph of liberal economic ideas has combined with technology to lower the cost and speed the impact of the movement of goods, people, money and ideas to an unimaginable degree. And on the whole, for the majority it has produced improvements in standards of living that do not require a sacrifice in quality of living.

The real questions to answer are how can you strike this balance without losing the benefits of dynamic trade, and how can you help the minority of countries and the minority within countries who are left behind when the growth in trade makes most people better off. I'm not sure that we will get those answers if the debate in developed countries becomes dominated by an undemocratic minority, however well-intentioned. Good governance does not mean that the minority is always right. Padraic Pearse once argued, stretching Burke's military metaphor, 'Always it is the many who fight for the Evil thing, and the few who fight for the Good thing; and always it is the few who win. For God fights with the small battalions'. 'Yes' and 'No' to that.

I should like more NGOs to accept open-mindedly that God is not always on their side. But such a cultural shift has to be earned. If democratic governments, representing majorities, composed of parties and creating international bodies through which to exercise some of their sovereignty, wish to encourage more responsibility in debate from NGOs and thereby revitalise democracy, then they have to lead the way in rearranging their relations with those same NGOs.

Political parties, so often out-numbered, out-financed and out-grown by NGOs, should try at local as well as national levels to create structures that enable interest groups to contribute fully to the party political debate. Governments need to open up the discussion on public policy, to tap the expertise of NGOs and to involve them – informed minorities – in a process whose end result will be determined by the majority. They should also involve NGOs far more in the delivery of services and not just the discussion of politics. International organisations have to be more open in the negotiation of global agreements, enabling civil society to participate in the process and to shape it. To their credit the World Bank have moved some way along this path, and after Seattle the World Trade Organisation clearly knows that it must do the same.

So to ensure that the debate on sustainable development is as constructive as possible, and that it delivers results that can both command majority consent and attract minority acquiescence, the rich, pluralist developed democracies need to understand that they have lessons of governance to learn as well. Good governance is not simply a subject on which the rich developed world can lecture poor developing countries. Behind these organisational and political shifts is a reaffirmation of the democratic spirit, the understanding that democracy is an adventure in dialogue, the attempt to persuade and secure consent, the belief in Adlai Stevenson's memorable phrase that average men and women are a great deal better than the average. We have lived through an era of political leadership as superstardom, the articulation of promises and solutions usually beyond the reach of even the most charismatic leaders, however many electoral terms they are awarded. Naturally, leaders can move things a little this way or that, for better or for worse. Yet I can't help thinking that human vanity these days should take second, sustainable place to a style of political leadership that recognises the value of persuasion over posturing, that knows that reason is the only long-term way to produce that aggregate of benign acts – a thousand and a thousand more – that alone can reverse the degradation of our world, its natural environment and for that matter its spiritual ideals.

What quaint notion is this – well, it may be quaint but it's not original. Six centuries before Christ, Lao Tzu, Chinese sage and Keeper of the Imperial Archives, wrote this:

> A leader is best
> When people barely know that he exists
> Not so good when people obey and proclaim him.
> 'Failure to honour people,
> They fail to honour you.'
> But a good leader, who talks little,
> When his work is done, his aim fulfilled,
> They will all say, 'We did this ourselves'

And what they will have done, if we are fortunate, is revitalise democracy to save our world, with its shadows of death and its shining lights, in all its fierce and awesome majesty.

2

Biodiversity

Tom Lovejoy

From the moment of our birth we grow up in a world of difference. Very early we learn we share this world not just with our family but with other living things. 'Every child has its bug period' as the great Harvard biologist E.O. Wilson says. We discover that not only are there different kinds of plants and animals – which scientists call species – but also that there can be lots of difference between individuals of any one kind.

This genetic variation we discover first in our parents. And unless we live in an urban setting far from a park, we soon learn that different kinds of animals and plants live together in different places: camels in deserts, whales in the seas, gorillas in tropical forests. The totality of this diversity from the genetic level, through organisms to ecosystems and landscapes is termed collectively biological diversity.

I chose to come to California because of an exciting experiment with biological diversity. I believe it may well help us in the global quest to maintain the biological underpinnings of sustainability, but I will turn to the story of the California gnatcatcher later in this talk. It is another fact of life that no organism can exist without affecting its environment. To be alive requires energy so all organisms need to eat: even green plants which use the energy of the sun have to take in nutrients to both live and grow. Similarly all organisms produce wastes. While they are biodegradable – and it is nothing short of astonishing what some organisms will 'feed' upon – the wastes do alter the environment and potentially affect other organisms.

Consequently the choice confronting humanity is not whether it affects the environment or does not. Rather the choice is about how we affect the environment, that is, in what ways and to what extent. Our planet is a living planet and its incredibly rich web of life is central to how it functions and therefore to sustainability of the human enterprise.

Understanding and attaining sustainability is therefore very complex and does not admit of many simple solutions. At the moment it is clear that we are far from sustainability. We are in deep trouble biologically and already into a spasm of extinction of our own making unequalled since the one which took the dinosaurs. It is not a peaceable kingdom. The rate at which species disappear is about 1,000 to 10,000 times normal, and a quarter or more of all species could vanish within a couple of decades. There is a major problem with biological diversity. That is a given. What is far more important is to recognise why it is happening and how we might arrange our lives so that our grandchildren can enjoy a sustainable existence on a biologically rich planet.

Biological diversity lies at the heart of sustainable development. The quality of our lives is entwined with it so much more deeply than most of us ever notice, that our fate depends on how well we provide for the future of other forms of life. This goes way beyond the obvious and essentials of food, fibre and shelter, to medicines and complex industrial processes. Biological diversity is essentially an incredibly vast library for the life sciences which is drawn upon to improve critical biologically based enterprises like agriculture and medicine. Just recently, a sample from a Zambezi riverbank of an obscure group of organisms called slime moulds yielded promising new compounds to fight tumors resistant to Taxol. Taxol, a key element in the arsenal against breast, ovarian and lung cancer, loses effectiveness in some cases. Taxol itself originally came from the

Pacific Yew, considered by foresters just a few years ago to be a trash tree in the forests of the northwest United States. The effective molecules in both cases came from natural defenses of the two wild species in interactions with other species. Sometimes the link is less direct but none the less very real, for example, the development of ACE inhibitors for treating high blood pressure arose from the discovery of a unknown system of regulation of blood pressure in the course of a study of the venom of a tropical viper.

The structure of ecosystems is made up of diverse kinds of plants, animals and micro-organisms, and their combined metabolisms constitute ecosystem function. In this day of quick resort to technological fixes, it is notable that New York City elected to restore the ecosystem function of its degrading watershed rather than construct a water-treatment plant. When I grew up in that city it was famous for the quality of its water: when I would return after being away I remember noticing how delicious the water tasted. It even won in blind tastings over fancy European bottled waters. But changes in land use in the watershed led to deteriorating water quality until our Environmental Protection Agency was about to require the city to build a multi-billion dollar water-treatment facility. Instead a bond issue at a tenth the cost made it possible to restore the watershed, its biological diversity, and therefore its functions. It was a natural and a permanent solution.

What we often call natural disasters are not always natural. They often happen where a little recognised ecosystem service, namely that of disaster prevention, has broken down. The horrifying floods and mudslides Hurricane Mitch brought Honduras and the even more ghastly events in December 1999 following heavy rains in Venezuela demonstrate this well. Equally heavy rains in Venezuela in 1952 had much lesser consequence because the poor – the ultimate victims – had not then deforested critical slopes. In Honduras there are anecdotes of adjacent hillsides in which the one with intact forest remained stable and also released less floodwater. Often characterised as 'natural disasters' these are only partly so, and the devastating humanitarian and economic blows make a strong argument for maintenance of ecosystems and their services. And, right now we are seeing this happen once again in Madagascar.

About fifty years ago, American freshwater ecologist Ruth Patrick began a line of research subsequently recognised by the US National Medal of Science. She began a systematic study of rivers and their biological diversity which demonstrates that the numbers and kinds of species in a river – its biological diversity in our current parlance – reflect the basic ecology of the river and the environmental stresses to which it is subject. In other words, biological diversity integrates the effects of all environmental problems affecting an ecosystem. This is essentially the fundamental, if often unrecognised, principle on which all environmental science and management is based. It applies everywhere not just in freshwater. Taken at the level of the entire globe, the Ruth Patrick Principle means that biological diversity can be considered the single measure of how humanity is affecting the environment. Instead of contemplating the welter of impacts society is generating, we now can measure the sum in a single number – a real measurable key to achieving and recognising sustainability.

At the scale of an ecosystem such as south Florida, the coastal sage scrub of California's five southern counties, or even as ambitious a one as the Amazon basin, the key consists of maintaining two elements – measurable elements – that are characteristic of the particular ecosystem. One is maintenance of ecosystem functions, such as the sheet flow of water in south Florida, and the other is maintenance of the biological diversity of the ecosystem. The latter can be thought of as managing so that the species list 100 or 500 years from now will be pretty much the same as it is today. It certainly does not mean that this has to be true of every spot within the ecosystem although there do need to be areas of strict preservation. There certainly can be locations (cities for example) where there is very intense use and low biological diversity. It does mean enough wild places and enough connections between them so all the species can survive in the long-term.

These two measurable goals provide an operational

definition for sustainable development within that piece of geography. It is, of course, seriously challenging because it means taking on all environmental problems intrinsic to the area as well as those like acid rain and climate change which are extrinsic. While this might seem to ignore the social and economic elements of sustainability, in the end it certainly does not, because otherwise they will begin to affect the two measurable standards: ecosystem function and biological diversity. Consequently other aspects like good governance and health, are also vital for success. If not applied late in a history of environmental degradation, this ecosystem management approach allows for considerable flexibility and creativity in addressing human aspirations.

South Florida provides an instructive case. A large ecological unit, it extends from the Kissimmee river and Lake Okeechobee about halfway up the Florida peninsula down through the Everglades Park and includes Florida Bay, the Florida Keys and the coral reef beyond. It is essentially a single system dependent upon the sheet flow of water from north to south known as the 'River of Grass'. Over a half century or more, individual isolated decisions – each presumably reasonable in their own context and time – for flood control, water supply and agricultural purposes, have drastically altered the flow. Not a drop of water flows naturally without a valve being turned, and only a quarter to a half of the natural flow reaches Florida Bay depending on the year.

Subterranean flow through the limestone under-pinnings is so reduced that the freshwater upwellings in Florida Bay have ceased. The result is a degrading ecosystem, reproductive failure of water birds, endangered species, hypersalinity in Florida Bay, loss of sea grass beds, algal blooms and additional stresses on an already stressed reef system. Ecosystem function and biological diversity are measurably impaired. I had no inkling of this when I first visited the Everglades as a teenager and the problems were not blatantly obvious at that point. In 1993, however, when I served as Science Advisor for the Department of the Interior, the problems were so obvious I could pick out some of them on satellite images of the peninsula.

If this is the consequence of ad hoc and uncoor-dinated decision-making, then the resolution of such problems, or better yet their avoidance, depends on the converse: on integrated and consultative decision-making that integrates society's decisions within the ecosystem framework. When it works best it takes the decision-making back to where people live. This is the essence of the multibillion dollar programme to restore the natural plumbing of south Florida as much as possible. It will take decades and makes a good case for avoiding such problems to begin with. It also is not easy with so many players with differing vested interests. For example the state recently refused to implement part of the plan, namely to buy out people who had encroached on some sensitive areas. Scientifically the plan needs some significant improvement. None the less, the degradation is beginning to be reversed and the overall trend seems positive.

Southern California presents a different example. Home to Los Angeles, San Diego and some of the worst urban/suburban sprawl in the United States, its native habitat had become reduced to the point that America's most powerful environmental legislation, the Endangered Species Act, was invoked on behalf of a jaunty little bird, the California gnatcatcher – which just happens to inhabit some of the priciest real estate in the nation. The powers of the Endangered Species Act have tended to be used only once a species is listed (an indication that its habitat and constituent biological diversity was on the verge of being endangered itself). So the exercise was not just about the gnatcatcher but an array of other species like a tiny arboreal salamander, a lizard known as the orange-throated whiptail and the San Diego Thornmint. Southern California, in fact, has a concentration of species found nowhere else; a biodiversity 'hotspot'. However, it seems nothing is done until a species reaches the brink of endangerment. Inevitably there are economic interests squared off against a species with an obscure name, so even though this really is a signal that the region is beginning to unravel biologically, the situation is easily caricatured as people versus biological esoterica.

When I was at the Department of the Interior, the situation in southern California was turning into a classic test case for a new approach. I came out to California and thanks to colleagues at the Department of Natural Resources, I had the chance to see the situation firsthand, from the air, on the ground and with the people seeking a resolution. This time the state of California, together with the federal agencies and the five county governments undertook to deal with the problem proactively while there was still some flexibility biologically and legally. Industry and civil society, especially the Nature Conservancy, were active participants. The idea was to plan conservation of entire natural communities before it was so late that costs and consequences became impossibly high. Large landowners, such as the Irvine Company, were major players, agreeing to land exchanges which worked for both nature and their business interests. At Camp Pendelton in San Diego County the United States Marine Corps worried that the military might have to shoulder a particular heavy burden and were delighted to discover that when all engaged in the plan this was not so. The Commandant even took particular pride in beach management to favour a nesting seabird.

Through the regional programme some 400,000 acres have been identified for eventual protection, a network of conservation which is now more than 60 per cent complete. True, endangered species listing of the gnatcatcher in one sense drove the process, but the result was considerably better than otherwise would have been the case using regulatory powers of the Endangered Species Act alone. In early 2000 California voters approved a $4 billion bond issue for securing critical conservation land, with at least $150 million of this dedicated to southern California.

I go to the Amazon with great frequency. As important as it is from a conservation point of view, I confess I also just like to go to this place of perpetual biological surprise and listen to howler monkeys and other jungle noises from my hammock. As complex as south Florida or southern California are, an even more complex challenge is presented by ecosystem management of the Amazon. Comprising eight nations, for none of whom the Amazon is a major priority, it none the less operates ecologically as a single system. In an extraordinary interaction between biological and physical elements, the Amazon literally generates half of its own rainfall. If too much forest is cleared in the wrong places, the hydrology would begin to change and affect the biology of this, the largest of the world's forests, the largest wilderness and the world's single greatest repository of biological diversity. In its vast river system, which contains 20 per cent of all the river water in the world, reside around 3,000 species of fish (more than the entire North Atlantic), some of which migrate from estuary to headwaters and back in the course of their life spans.

Each Amazonian nation finds it hard enough to integrate the various elements of government decision-making into a comprehensive policy resembling something like ecosystem management for their piece of the Amazon. Is there any possibility that there could be coordination at the level of the Amazon as a whole? The optimistic answer is that there is certainly a greater chance today with some enlightened national leaders and ministers. The Treaty for Amazon Cooperation provides a possible framework, but it will require leadership, especially by Brazil, which holds two-thirds of the real estate. I believe it could happen and I know that multilateral agencies like the World Bank, the Inter-American Development Bank, UNDP and UNEP plus civil society would jump at the chance to support such an effort. Sustainable development takes good governance as well as good science.

All three examples must be considered works in progress not final solutions because environmental problems arise continuously like dragons' teeth. One of the most important extrinsic factors for ecosystem management is that of climate change. This is, in large degree, because when biological diversity is protected by isolated parks and reserves, the ability of species to move and to track required ecological conditions is impeded by an obstacle course of human-dominated landscapes.

All will be for naught if society fails to address the

greenhouse gas problem. The threat is much more imminent than most people realise. The world is literally melting: tropical glaciers will be gone in twenty years and new data on the Arctic ice cap indicate that it too is likely to break up in the same time period. The good news is that there are things we can do about that right now. Some involve energy substitution and conservation. Others involve trees and forests because they play an enormous role in the global carbon cycle. A major effort to stem deforestation, reforest, and to protect natural forests will ward off further greenhouse gas emissions and also make a major contribution to conservation of biological diversity.

The moment is at hand to take the right steps to underpin a sustainable future biologically. Certainly, the challenge is highly complex, and it must work locally everywhere so that it all adds up to sustainable development. Yet it could be summed up by saying we need to live within nature rather than think of it as something which is taken care of, almost in token fashion, with fenced off areas while humanity operates without restraint in the rest of the landscape. As powerful and imperative as I believe the practical arguments for conservation are, a change in perception and value about our place in nature could achieve vastly more. Classical conservation is not in fact enough. Honouring the Patrick Principle through ecosystem management means we have to live in ways that won't degrade the biology of areas of strict preservation, and also that we won't degrade the landscapes in which we live. That is why sustainable development is so important. It is also why it is so complex to grasp. Fortunately in biological diversity, we not only have wonderful resources we also have a very real measure of sustainability. I am frequently reminded of a long discussion with British naturalist Gerald Durrell during which he turned to me with tears in his eyes and said: 'There is so little time'.

The natural world in which we live is nothing short of entrancing – wondrous really. Personally, I take great joy in sharing a world with the shimmering variety of life on earth. Nor can I believe any of us really want a planet which is a lonely wasteland.

3

Business

John Browne

Is genuine progress still possible? Is development sustainable? Or is one strand of progress – industrialisation – now doing such damage to the environment that the next generation won't have a world worth living in?

Concern over future sustainability is not new. There has always been something which appeared to threaten it – fears that the world would run out of wood, coal, oil or fertile land. And at such times there were, as now, people who responded constructively and optimistically to such challenges – while others were fatalistic – willing to accept decline rather than determined to reverse it. Are we just rerunning history, a moment which, in retrospect, will seem to future generations no different from those of the past? I'd like to be able to say 'yes'. But the answer, I'm afraid, is 'no'. No, because the challenges are now more numerous and more complex. No, because the necessary answers can't be reduced to a single breakthrough.

Fifty years ago, Bertrand Russell broadcasting the first Reith lecture did so to a nation that accepted the potential and the need for economic growth. But today the potential for growth itself is in question. There is a fundamental concern about the limits to growth, and a feeling that the way we now live is not sustainable. America still remains predominantly optimistic but in Europe in particular, including Britain, opinion surveys show that almost half the population have lost their faith in progress. Material living standards may be rising but very large numbers of people no longer believe that the world of tomorrow will be a better place in which to live. Why? What has created this pessimism? It seems more and more clear to me when I travel worldwide that it is the cumulative impact of key factors such as the pressures of population growth; the pressures of urbanisation; water shortages; environmental challenges; the quality of the air we breathe; the pollution of oceans; the loss of species as habitats are transformed. The gathering evidence of a fundamental change to the climate caused by human activity.

Sustainability is about the environment and biodiversity, but there are other factors as well. The pressures created by a world in which global markets operate for twenty-four hours a day, seven days a week and by the removal of the comfort and protection of the old ways of working. It is as if history were constantly accelerating. We are in a world without certainty – except for the certainty of change. A world where national cultures and the credibility of institutions of democracy are challenged by global competitive pressures. The uncertainty and fatalism is also fuelled by doubts about science itself. Some of its uses – such as the genetic modification of crops – produce huge public scepticism and even fear. US opinion continues to believe that progress is directly associated with the advance of technology, while in Europe two-thirds of people are sceptical of the link. What can a businessman say or do in response to these challenges?

Perhaps I am expected to make the speech of the accused standing in the dock. That's not how I see it. I believe business is constructively engaged in resolving these problems and that changes in technology and in the way the global economy works are giving the means to deliver genuine progress. If I had to plead from the dock that would be the essence of my case. And it is certainly my motivation. Business is not in opposition to, but has a fundamental role in delivering sustainable development to meet the needs of today's world without depriving future generations of their means to do so. That's a strong assertion and for some counterintuitive. It has to be justified by something more than an assurance of good intentions. In essence it is about enlightened self-interest.

The simple fact is that business needs sustainable societies in order to protect its own sustainability. All the concerns summarised are issues for business too. Few businesses are short-term activities. Most want to do business again and again over many decades. And this is especially true of the businesses which are most often criticised, those, like mine, which are in the business of extracting and developing the world's natural resources. We are by definition long-term players. We have to live with the consequences of what we do for decades. We can't pack up and go home when the going gets tough. But in order to sustain what we value, we have to be prepared to change. And the sort of change which business promotes is the application of technical advances to meet human needs.

Historically, all the fears of shortage, of food, of water, of land, were disproved by change, by technical breakthroughs which substituted one thing for another, and through fundamental shifts in productivity which moved the boundaries of the possible. Now, to an unprecedented extent, technology has the ability to repeat that process, embracing a radical and transforming change beyond all previous experience. In other words not a rerun of history but something very different.

We face a revolution in the way the economy works

driven by new technology. A revolution which will have major beneficial consequences for the environment. I think of it as a 'connected economy' but connected in ways we have never known before. Connected not just from one person or company to another, from one buyer to one seller, but connected as the brain is connected, as a network of multiple and simultaneous linkages. The connected economy is beginning to give us the ability to create new marketplaces and to integrate and manage complex systems at a distance and with great precision and speed. It is also giving us the ability to spread and share knowledge instantly.

What has all that got to do with the environmental challenges we're facing? The shift in productivity is dramatically changing the way in which resources are being used. One of the first projects I was involved in as a young graduate was the development of the Forties field in the North Sea, over two billion barrels of oil in hostile waters 100 miles from Aberdeen. That development, which itself was revolutionary at the time, required the construction of four large platforms from which the wells went down to extract the oil 7,000 feet below sea level, requiring 56,000 tons of steel. Now, a similar development could be done with a single platform, because technical advances allow us to drill horizontally under the seabed for up to seven miles. That drilling is not random. Thanks to modern computing and communication we can now steer the drill bit in real time, with information feeding back to a computer screen onshore in Aberdeen as the drilling tip goes through the rocks offshore. But, the connected economy isn't just about productivity, it is also about learning and the way in which knowledge and best practice can be developed, disseminated and applied on a global basis. This, after all, is one of the great benefits of globalisation.

One way of seeing this is to focus on the problems at the very heart of environmental concern: climate change or global warming and the quality of air in the world's cities. The latest authoritative scientific reports on climate change make clear, in the most careful, rigorous language, that indications of a human effect on the climate are mounting. The research goes on. The conclusions so far, of course, are provisional but then as Karl Popper has noted, 'almost all science is provisional', research never ends. In the real world we have to act on the balance of the available evidence, and everyone has to do what is in their power to confront the issue. Precautionary action is justified, and even those who disagree should recognise that in a world where knowledge is openly available, the scope to carry on denying a widely perceived problem is very limited. Whilst some advocate doing nothing, others advocate doing anything. Climate change requires a measured approach that tackles the environmental threat without undermining economic growth. Those who seek to use climate change to push an anti-business agenda damage the prospects for partnership. We're in this together. Theatrical gestures are no substitute for concerted action to find solutions.

What can be done? We are progressively extending our knowledge of how to reduce emissions. Ten or twenty years ago, the oil industry was symbolised by the flares which shone above our platforms. My company's aim is now to eliminate this practice during the next three years, except on the rare occasions when safety is in question. The transfer of crude oil from pipeline to tankers in the Firth of Forth caused emissions of as much as 80 tons per day. Now, thanks to technical advance, we have a facility which captures all those emissions. And that is also one technology which will spread around the world as more will work through the clean development mechanisms of the Kyoto Agreement. Another example relates to a natural gas project in Wyoming and New Mexico which will realise a saving of more than 20,000 tons of methane annually, the equivalent to reducing carbon dioxide emissions by more than 430,000 tons.

Steps like these are significant contributions to the goal of our company, which is to reduce the emissions of greenhouse gases from all our operations by at least 10 per cent from a 1990 baseline by 2010 and within a single year we have already achieved almost a 4 per cent reduction. And we're not alone. Many, many other companies are taking constructive steps in the same direction. Shell has just announced plans to build a pilot emission-free gas-fired power station in Norway.

The second key issue on which to focus is the more immediate reality of air quality, a primary issue of environmental concern to people around the world and particularly those who live in cities. There are numerous causes, of which the transport sector is just one. But again, we can't cross the road and pretend the problem doesn't exist. Our role is about applying technology to produce fuels which are cleaner. The process is progressive and continuous. For example, we are offering cleaner fuels thanks to advances in refining technology at places such as Grangemouth. We've eliminated lead and lowered sulphur and benzene levels in our diesel and gasoline throughout the United Kingdom. We will be selling cleaner fuels in over forty big cities around the world by the end of this year. Technology is delivering.

That in itself is part of the business process, to start from what you know, to deliver that, to spread best practice using all the technology now available, and simultaneously to learn from experience. And to look for the next step. It is impossible to predict the next steps with any precision, but some possibilities are already becoming evident. The mix of fuels used to produce energy will continue to change. The opportunity, for instance, to substitute natural gas as the dominant fuel source in power generation. That will build on the dramatic advances in the efficiency of turbines which make gas the fuel of choice in both economic and environmental terms. Or the opportunity to produce cars with engines and fuels designed together in ways which would eliminate virtually all emissions. We and others are working on that with like-minded people in the car industry. And in the medium-term, to expand the opportunity to produce energy commercially from photo-voltaic power and in the longer run from hydrogen, the cleanest of all fuels.

Technological change will help us avoid the harsh trade-off which some deem inevitable, between the desire to increase living standards and the desire to preserve a clean environment. But only if we don't kill off our ability to develop new technology. Sustainable development requires successful companies. The question to the accused is whether business can be trusted to do all this? I believe it is the connected nature of four crucial relationships in which we are involved: with our employees, with our customers, with our shareholders and the public, and with governments. The first is internal – with our employees – 80,000 people worldwide in our case. These people care enormously about these issues. They are citizens too. They have families and they have hopes and fears about the future. Companies are only as good as the people who work for them. The people who make up and shape society are the same sorts of people who work in companies like my own. When we are competing for the brains and the energy of the brightest and the best against the fashionable and apparently lucrative world of the dot.coms we do not ignore the values of society and particularly of that new generation. People want to work for something they believe in and to make a contribution to the progress of the world in which they live. And if business is to succeed it has to offer them the opportunity to do just that. That is why our commercial targets now embrace environmental and ethical objectives. They do so partly because our employees demand it. And our customers demand it too. We are all part of a society which wishes to protect sustainability. We have a shared responsibility.

Let me now turn to the relationship with shareholders and the public and how this underpins trust. An old Russian proverb, quoted by President Reagan to President Gorbachev during a summit on nuclear disarmament captures this perfectly, 'trust but verify'. Companies are radically altering their annual reports to include detailed information about environmental and social performance alongside their financial accounts. Performance is now measured on many dimensions and success is defined in a holistic way. This new approach to corporate reporting is also entirely consistent with the economic revolution which is now upon us. One of the great gains from the connected economy is transparency because that is the key to confidence and trust, and to the granting of permission by society for companies to pursue their activities and to continue to make progress. It is that sort of transparency which will overcome the scepticism and doubts which exist about science and about the linkage between technical advance and genuine progress. Transparency is not just about publishing numbers. It is also about establishing clarity as to where responsibility lies. This goes to the very heart of relationships with government. It is said that the power of companies has increased while the power of governments has declined. I don't think it is quite so simple. As Bertrand Russell once said, 'from any single perspective power always seems to be elsewhere' and that is truer than ever in a connected economy, where every decision is dependent on the decisions of others.

There are some issues which companies should not decide, and where instead we should seek agreement at governmental levels to set some rules and standards. For instance, should exploration and development in pristine and other sensitive areas of the world be permitted? Companies have a duty to participate in this debate, particularly when it comes to discussing how developments can best be carried out. But whether an area currently closed for development should remain closed forever, or remain a development option for the future, is a matter where the final decision should be left with governments. We have a duty to inform the debate, but not to resolve it.

It would be disingenuous to pretend there isn't a problem here. If companies themselves unilaterally close the option, and take the decision that should be taken democratically, they run the risk of suffering competitive disadvantage when less scrupulous companies subsequently step into their place and seize the opportunity if and when it becomes available. In this connected economy companies and governments both need to honour their responsibilities.

This relationship should give society the confidence to trust business to deliver sustainable development, on the basis of enlightened self-interest. But, of course, this means that companies must play their full role. If one were to listen to our sternest critics, these progressive initiatives – such as reducing emissions – shouldn't be happening, because they cost money and they offer no immediate commercial return. They would argue that competitive and commercial pressures militate against such measures. And they would say this is why some countries and companies are unwilling to move in this direction. But that is to take a very narrow and limited view of what is in our interest. In my view, such measures are not only desirable on social grounds, they also make perfect business sense.

The enlightened company increasingly recognises that there are good commercial reasons for being ahead of the pack when it comes to issues to do with the environment. Of course there are valid concerns which exist over the role of business. The track record is mixed and enlightenment is not universal. But look objectively at both the technical progress which is being made, and at the impact on business behaviour of the connected, knowledge driven economy the judgement must come down in favour of optimism. I remain an optimist not because I deny the problems: they are real and substantial; nor because I believe that the existing pattern and structure of development can be sustained – it clearly can't and shouldn't be; but because I believe that sustainability is built on change, as it always has been. Without a green revolution the world couldn't have fed the two billion extra citizens who have added to its population since 1960. Without the investment in basic engineering which provided sewerage systems and clean water, the towns and cities of the world would have been overwhelmed by sickness and disease.

Sustainability is not about freezing a system at a particular moment in time. It is about recognising where the system is close to reaching the limits of its capacity and acting to forestall those risks. And that requires constructive engagement from us all. My optimism springs from the fact that such positive change is happening all the time around us. That is what makes now such an exciting time to be alive.

4

Health and Population

Gro Harlem Brundtland

In October last year, the UN Secretary General Kofi Annan went to a hospital in Sarajevo to welcome 'baby number six billion'. Nobody – and least of all the Secretary General – would deny that the choice of Fatima Mevic's baby, born just after midnight on 12 October, had more to do with the Secretary General's travel schedule than with demographics. We can imagine that Mr and Mrs Mevic were rather bemused about all the fuss surrounding their little baby boy. The key point, though, is that Kofi Annan's purpose was not to talk about numbers. For the Secretary General, this birth was an occasion to focus on a different moral issue. He said that the 'Day of Six Billion' challenged us all 'to live up to the promise of our time to give every man, woman and child an opportunity to make the most of their abilities, in safety and in dignity.'

I share his view. More than that, I have a mission. I want the fight against poverty to be our global cause as we straddle the millennium. Our goal must be to create a world where we all can live, well-fed and clothed, and with dignity. We must do this without undermining future generations' ability to do the same. I believe that poor people will only be able to prosper, and emerge from poverty, if they enjoy better health. I want health to be at the heart of our struggle for sustainable development.

About three billion people live on less than two dollars a day. In other words, half of the global population do not have anything close to a decent standard of living. That means that three billion people live in such poverty that they cannot afford proper housing, proper healthcare or proper education for their children. Almost half of those people live on less than one dollar per day. That means more than a billion people not having enough to eat every day and at constant risk of malnutrition.

Poverty has a woman's face; of the 1.3 billion poorest, only 30 per cent are male. Poor women are often caught in a damaging cycle of malnutrition and disease. This plight stems directly from women's place in the home and in society. Also, it often reflects gender bias in healthcare. Women from poor households are more than a hundred times more likely to die as a result of childbirth than their wealthier counterparts.

Over the past few years, the human development index has declined in more than thirty countries. Almost one-third of all children are undernourished. The average African household consumes 20 per cent less today than it did twenty-five years ago! And development assistance is falling too. Only a few countries have fulfilled past commitments to provide 0.7 per cent of their GDP for development assistance. In actual fact the world average is now closer to 0.2 per cent.

Beyond the dry statistics lies tragedy. During 1999, when I visited Africa, I saw firsthand the malnourished children and the despair that follows from some of the conflicts that rage in this continent. These are not so much territorial disputes as they are rooted in general misery, the aftermath of humanitarian crises, shortages of food and water and the spreading of poverty and ill-health.

In a number of mega-cities around the world, the quality of life among the five, ten, fifteen million people and the poor who scrape out a living in their vast slums is dismal. The noise, pollution, squalor and dangers for those who have made their cardboard housing underneath the large overpasses make modern living for the poor seem like a latter-day realisation of Hell. The damage from pollution and the continuous threat of violence add to the infectious diseases which always leave their deepest imprint on poor people's lives.

Most of us agree that this state of affairs is unacceptable. Yet still we do little or nothing about it. The rich have lived next door to appalling squalor for centuries without being sufficiently disturbed to take any action. But now, in our global economy, this may be beginning to change.

Over the past twenty-five years, population growth in many countries has slowed rather faster than demographers had first expected, especially in east Asia. Thanks to this slowing down, the experts now believe the earth's population will stabilise around nine billion, rather than twelve to fifteen billion as some feared. At the same time, the world's capacity to produce food has grown at a fantastic rate, as a result of new grain varieties and economic incentives to producers. In 1989 the Vietnamese government allowed farmers to sell their rice freely on the market, encouraging new seed varieties and farming techniques. Within two years, Vietnam went from having to import rice to becoming the world's second largest exporter.

The structure of societies is also changing. Young adults in India, Algeria and Iran struggle to find jobs, to earn an income and to see a hope for the future. The governments of Japan, Sweden and Spain struggle to find answers to a rapidly ageing population, and to the challenge this poses for their production and welfare systems. Ironically, many developing and middle-income countries are caught with both problems: they face a swelling population of older folk, while they still have to cope with population growth.

Years of observation and experience have shown that families living in freedom and given the opportunity to fulfil their basic needs, have fewer children. These children are more likely to be healthy and educated. Societies that have satisfied the basic needs of their populations tend to reduce pollution and environmental destruction. As population structures change, the role of the State becomes clearer: to empower people to make meaningful choices; to create a supportive environment for families; to look after the interests of children, for they are the future. These principles are as relevant in India as they are in Norway, or indeed anywhere in the world.

None of this should surprise us. Ground-breaking consensus was reached six years ago, when the International Conference on Development and Population, in Cairo, firmly established that development, poverty reduction and respect for women's reproductive rights are vital to stabilising the world's population. We do not yet, however, have a consensus about the importance of good health in global development. Europe learned about the existence of infectious agents around the middle of the nineteenth century. The importance of hygiene and clean water became apparent. The rich finally began to do something about the dreadful slums that surrounded their wealthy areas. It was self-interest that finally prompted action. As hygiene and healthcare improved, the average life expectancy increased by nearly twenty years in many countries. Following this development was the huge industrial push that brought the current wealth and affluence to the West and practically eradicated absolute poverty from most of Europe.

Unfortunately, the fear of disease that scared politicians, city planners and corporate leaders to invest in health and sanitation for the populations of Europe did not then extend as far as to their former colonies and the other countries far away from their own cities. Again, as in the nineteenth century, it is self-interest that lies at the heart of this change. In the modern world, bacteria and viruses travel almost as fast as money. With globalisation, a single microbial sea washes all of humankind. There are no health sanctuaries. Diseases cannot be kept out of even the richest of countries by rearguard defensive action. The separation between domestic and international health problems is no longer useful, as people and goods travel across continents. Two million people cross international borders every single day, about a tenth of humanity each year. And of these, more than a million travel from developing to industrialised countries each week. This is an accelerating trend, and is not likely to be reversed. I suggest 'health security' is as important as national security. Threats to health undermine what I call our 'human security'. The levels of ill-health experienced by most of the world's people threatens their countries' economic and political viability: this, in turn, affects economic and political interests of all other countries.

Interestingly enough, it is not only infectious diseases that spread with globalisation. Changes in lifestyle and diet have prompted an increase in heart disease, diabetes and cancer. More than anything, tobacco is sweeping the globe as it is criss-crossed by market forces. Only weeks after the old socialist economies in Europe and Asia opened up to Western goods and capital, camels and cowboys began to appear on buildings and billboards. Those who think that tobacco-related death and disease is mainly a burden for rich countries are mistaken. If the growth in tobacco use goes unchecked, the numbers of deaths related to its use will nearly triple, from four million each year today to ten million each year in thirty years. More than 70 per cent of this increase will take place in the developing countries.

People in most rich and middle income countries have come to expect much better standards of health in the past fifty years. In that time we have failed miserably in securing even a basic level of health among the three billion who are poor. In the interval, some of their health problems have become even more difficult to solve. Recently, in Mozambique, I saw children whose eyes were glazed with fever from a strand of malaria that could have been prevented if their parents could have afforded bed nets. Deforestation has changed malaria from a nuisance to a curse in a matter of twenty years. More people are suffering from this killing and debilitating disease now than ever before, and deforestation, climate change and breakdowns in health services have caused the disease to spread to new areas and areas that have been malaria-free for decades, like Europe.

In the Philippines, I have watched how beggars sit exhausted on the pavements convulsed with coughing. Tuberculosis, which we long believed had been brought under control by effective treatment, is on the rise again. Increasingly, we see forms of tuberculosis which are resistant to all but a very expensive cocktail of drugs. While HIV and AIDS may be the most serious threat to face sub-Saharan Africa and other developing regions. Already, the AIDS epidemic is the leading cause of death in several African countries. AIDS has reversed the increases in life expectancy we have seen over the past thirty years. The social and economic devastation in countries that could lose a fifth of their productive populations is heart-rending.

We are facing this alarming situation largely because of an outdated approach to development. Our theories have to catch up with what our ears and eyes are telling us – and quickly. There was a period in development thinking when spending on public services, such as health and education, would have to wait. Good health was a luxury, only to be achieved when countries had developed a particular level of physical infrastructure and established a certain economic strength. The implicit assumption was that health was to do with consumption. Experience and research over the past few years have shown that such thinking was at best simplistic and at worst plainly wrong. I maintain that if people's health improves, they make a real contribution to their nation's prosperity. Good health is not only an important concern for individuals, it plays a central role in achieving sustainable economic growth and an effective use of resources.

As in Europe at the end of the nineteenth and beginning of the twentieth century, we have seen that developing countries which invest relatively more on health are likely to achieve higher economic growth. In East Asia, for example, life expectancy increased by over eighteen years in the two decades that preceded the most dramatic economic take-off in history. A recent analysis for the Asian Development Bank concluded that a third of the phenomenal Asian economic growth between 1965 and 1997 resulted from these gains.

We all fear the spread of disease and, increasingly, corporations appreciate the market opportunities provided by affluent populations. This encourages investment in health as a means of reducing poverty. Globalisation is about much more than trade. It is about communicating with an infinity of new people, about relating to them – and therefore also getting involved in their lives. The company which sets up a production plant in Vietnam or Peru may do so based on an evaluation of economic opportunities, but it will soon find itself having to relate to the political, social and economic reality of the country. A large engineering company ran an advertising campaign some time ago saying that being global meant being local worldwide. Companies that show commitment to the countries and communities they work with find that they are better appreciated – whether by prime ministers or their own workforce. Productivity increases too. A company that deals with developing countries has to confront the challenge of poverty and ill-health. A company's stock price can fall on Wall Street because workers in a subsidiary's plant in Malaysia are not provided with health insurance. As communication and social activism become globalised, large companies find that labour standards are important. Ignoring them can be costly both to public image and stock price.

New technology, almost inflation-less growth and soaring stock markets in many Western countries have created a dizzying sensation that the old rules don't apply anymore. Sometimes I wonder what has happened to the ideologies that used to guide us. Marx is dead, Adam Smith is certainly gone, and so it seems has every economist who ever provided any rules for decision-makers to follow. For pessimists, there may be much to worry about, but for anyone with belief in human creativity, these are times of opportunity. Several countries, including the United States, now recognise that improving international levels of health is a matter of national security. Earlier this year, the Security Council met and discussed the global AIDS epidemic. The rationale for debating global health, has indeed changed. Also, with less than four hundred billionaires holding assets that equal the cumulative worth of 45 per cent of the world's population, we start to see a change in the flow of resources for poverty reduction. There are many implications of this extremely skewed distribution of wealth. One positive one is the emergence, among these billionaires, of individuals who have philanthropic ambitions. Any one of them could singlehandedly cover the cost of eradicating, or at least controlling, a life-threatening disease.

Unorthodox new alliances are being forged to support human development. Industry and international agencies are coming together to find ways to get medicines and vaccines to those who cannot afford to pay. They have established new partnerships to fight malaria, river blindness and leprosy. As they reform their healthcare systems, governments build networks that involve the private and voluntary sectors to get vital services to people in need. We need to bring the new approaches into the mainstream of development activity. Many international organisations still have no adequate mechanisms for working beyond the country level, reaching directly to communities in need. We also find it hard to work for people ruled by corrupt despots, by weak leaders caught up in power-struggles, or by plain warlords. However, as has already been argued, sustainable development cannot work without good governance.

The Nobel economics prize laureate Amartya Sen defines poverty as 'deprivation of capability'. He argues that people are poor not only because their income is low, but because they do not have access to basic services, such as health and education, which would have increased their freedom. Poverty, he says, seriously deprives people of a number of choices they must have available in order to live a satisfying life. This must be right. If you don't have an adequate form of health insurance, becoming ill means becoming poorer, both directly, because you have to spend part of your income to pay for treatment and medicines, and indirectly, because your choices become even more limited.

The challenge is to look at the world through the eyes, and spirit of the poor. Simply, poor people all over the world dread being ill. It can so easily be a disaster. It can throw a whole family into destitution. Poor people have very limited choices. Medicine costs, fees charged by health workers and transport costs quickly eat into whatever funds are available.

A rickshaw driver in Khulna, Bangladesh, may well

appreciate that he lives in a place where the risk of tuberculosis is high. But his poverty deprives him of the choice to live somewhere else. When he gets infected, he cannot compete so well for work. His income goes down. This sends the family into a spiral of debt and increasing poverty. His children – particularly the girls – may be kept from school. The family may have to cut out fish from their meals most days. Their malnutrition increases vulnerability to illness – and the risk of death. Being too poor to go to an ordinary bank, the family has to borrow from loan sharks who take perhaps 20 per cent interest, perhaps 60 per cent or more, in order to pay for medicines. With such costs, our rickshaw driver understandably chooses to cut the treatment as soon as the fever goes down and he feels better. It is likely that the infection will return, though next time resistant to the normal drugs used for treatment. The health of others, who live nearby, is in real danger.

It does not have to be like this. There are examples of TB programmes that work properly for poor people. They would help our rickshaw driver to be cured in six or nine months, and enable him to get back to work – non-infectious – within weeks. He would be able to avoid crippling debt. He would not need to take his children out of school. His own poverty, and that of his family, would be reduced. Take another example. Plantation workers in Indonesia were treated for chronic anaemia which has been reported to result in a 20 per cent rise in productivity, increasing the earnings of the workers and the output of the plantation.

Relatively simple health interventions, like effective treatment for TB, getting a bed net against malaria in every African household, eradicating polio, or providing an integrated child health programme, can ensure that children are healthy and well nourished. They also improve the economic situation and productivity of individual households. Quite simply, we have – in our hands – a concrete, result-orientated and measurable way of starting to reduce poverty. To complete the task, education and infrastructure should improve. Private investment and trade must increase. But good health is a prerequisite. Unless we help improve the health of the world's poorest billion and a half people, they are destined to live lives of continuing poverty.

All this means that health must be moved from the periphery of the development process to the centre, where it belongs. The health minister must not sit at the far end of the Cabinet table, but be up there next to the prime minister or president, together with the finance minister and planning and industry minister. In developing countries, they often cannot even be found at the Cabinet table. This, surely, is where they are most needed.

Are we ready to scale up our investments in poor people's health? Are we ready to make investments vital for sustainable development? Great advances in healthcare have been made over the past 100 years. Our generation risks going down in history as the one that allowed the hard-won health achievements of the twentieth century to be lost – lost because it decided to ignore the billion and a half people who had been excluded from the health revolution. The evidence is there – and so are the opportunities.

5

Poverty and Globalisation

Vandana Shiva

Recently, I was visiting Bhatinda in Punjab because of an epidemic of farmers' suicides. Punjab used to be the most prosperous agricultural region in India. Today every farmer is in debt and despair. Vast stretches of land have become waterlogged desert. And as an old farmer pointed out, even the trees have stopped bearing fruit because the heavy use of pesticides has killed the pollinators – the bees and butterflies.

And Punjab is not alone in experiencing this ecological and social disaster. Last year I was in Warangal, Andhra Pradesh, where farmers have also been committing suicide. Farmers who traditionally grew pulses and millets and paddy have been lured by seed companies to buy hybrid cotton seeds referred to by the seed merchants as 'white gold', which were supposed to make them millionaires. Instead they became paupers. Their native seeds have been displaced with new hybrids which cannot be saved and need to be purchased every year at high cost. Hybrids are also very vulnerable to pest attacks. Spending on pesticides in Warangal has shot up 2000 per cent from $2.5 million in the 1980s to $50 million in 1997. Now farmers are consuming the same pesticides as a way of killing themselves so that they can escape permanently from unpayable debt.

On 27 March, twenty-five-year-old Betavati Ratan took his life because he could not pay back debts for drilling a deep tube well on his two-acre farm. The well is now dry, as are the wells in Gujarat and Rajasthan where more than fifty million people face a water famine. The drought is not a 'natural disaster'. It is 'man-made'. It is the result of mining of scarce groundwater in arid regions to grow thirsty cash crops for export instead of water-prudent food crops for local needs.

It is experiences such as these which tell me that we are so wrong to be smug about the new global economy. It is time to stop and think about the impact of globalisation on the lives of ordinary people. This is vital to achieve sustainability. Seattle and the World Trade Organisation protests last year forced everyone to think again. People refer to different aspects of sustainable development taking globalisation for granted, while for me it is now time to re-evaluate what we are doing. For what we are doing in the name of globalisation is, to the poor, brutal and unforgivable. This is especially evident in India as we witness the unfolding disasters of globalisation, especially with respect to food and agriculture.

Who feeds the world? It is women and small farmers working with biodiversity who are the primary food providers in the Third World, and, contrary to the dominant assumption, their biodiversity-based small farms are more productive than industrial monocultures. The rich diversity and sustainable systems of food production are being destroyed in the name of increasing food production. However, with the destruction of diversity, rich sources of nutrition disappear. When measured in terms of nutrition per acre, and from the perspective biodiversity, the so-called 'high yields' of industrial agriculture or industrial fisheries do not imply more production of food and nutrition.

Yield usually refers to production per unit area of a single crop. Output refers to the total production of diverse crops and products. Planting only one crop in the entire field as a monoculture will, of course, increase its individual yield. Planting multiple crops in a mixture will have low yields of individual crops, but will have high total output of food. Yields have been defined in such a way as to make the food production on small farms by small farmers disappear. This hides the production by millions of women farmers in the Third World – farmers like those in Himalaya who fought against logging in the Chipko movement and who in their terraced fields even today grow jhangora (barnyard millet), marsha (amaranth), tur (pigeon pea), urad (black gram), gahat (horse gram), soya bean (glycine max) and bhat (glycine soya) – an endless diversity. From the biodiversity perspective, biodiversity-based productivity is higher than monoculture productivity. I call this blindness to the high productivity of diversity a 'monoculture of the mind', which creates monocultures in our fields and in our world.

The Mayan peasants in the Chiapas are characterised as unproductive because they produce only 2 tons of corn per acre. However, the overall food output is 20 tons per acre when the diversity of their beans and squashes, their vegetables and their fruit trees are taken into account.

In Java, small farmers cultivate 607 species in their home gardens. In sub-Saharan Africa, women cultivate 120 different plants. A single home garden in Thailand has 230 species, and African home gardens have more than sixty species of trees.

Rural families in the Congo eat leaves from more than fifty species of their farm trees.

A study in eastern Nigeria found that home gardens occupying only 2 per cent of a household's farmland accounted for half of the farm's total output.

In Indonesia 20 per cent of household income and 40 per cent of domestic food supplies come from the home gardens managed by women.

Research done by FAO has shown that small bio-diverse farms can produce thousands of times more food than large, industrial monocultures. And diversity in addition to giving more food, is the best strategy for preventing drought and desertification. What the world needs to feed a growing population sustainably is bio-diversity intensification, not the chemical intensification or the intensification of genetic engineering. While women and small peasants feed the world through bio-diversity we are repeatedly told that without genetic engineering and globalisation of agriculture the world will starve. In spite of all empirical evidence showing that genetic engineering does not produce more food and, in fact, often leads to a yield decline, it is constantly promoted as the only alternative available for feeding the hungry.

This deliberate blindness to diversity, the blindness to nature's production, production by women, production by Third World farmers allows destruction and appropriation to be projected as creation. Take the case of the much flouted 'golden rice', or genetically engineered vitamin A rice, as a cure for blindness. It is assumed that without genetic engineering we cannot remove vitamin A deficiency. However, nature gives us abundant and diverse sources of vitamin A. If rice was not polished, rice itself would provide vitamin A. If herbicides were not sprayed on our wheat fields, we would have bathua, amaranth and mustard leaves as delicious and nutritious greens that provide vitamin A. Women in Bengal use more than 150 plants as greens; hinche sak (enhydra fluctuans), palang sak (spinacea oleracea), tak palang (rumex vesicarious), lal sak (amaranthus gangeticus) to name but a few. But the myth of creation presents biotechnologists as the creators of vitamin A, negating nature's diverse gifts and women's knowledge of how to use this diversity to feed their children and families.

The most efficient means of rendering the destruction of nature, local economies and small autonomous producers is by rendering their production invisible. Women who produce for their families and communities are treated as 'non-productive' and 'economically' inactive. The devaluation of women's work, and of work done in sustainable economies, is the natural outcome of a system constructed by capitalist patriarchy. This is how globalisation destroys local economies and destruction itself is counted as growth. And women themselves are devalued. Because many women in the rural and indigenous communities work co-operatively with nature's processes, their work is often contradictory to the dominant market driven 'development' and trade policies. And because work that satisfies needs and ensures sustenance is devalued in general, there is less nurturing of life and life support systems.

The devaluation and invisibility of sustainable, regenerative production is most glaring in the area of food. While patriarchal division of labour has assigned women the role of feeding their families and communities, patriarchal economics and patriarchal views of science and technology magically make women's work in providing food disappear. 'Feeding the World' becomes disassociated from the women who actually do it and is projected as dependent on global agribusiness and biotechnology corporations. However, industrialisation and genetic engineering of food and globalisation of trade in agriculture are recipes for creating hunger, not for feeding the poor. Everywhere, food production is becoming a negative economy, with farmers spending more to buy costly inputs for industrial production than the price they receive for their produce. The consequence is rising debts and epidemics of suicides in both poor and rich countries.

Economic globalisation is leading to a concentration of the seed industry, increased use of pesticides, and, finally, increased debt. Capital-intensive, corporate-controlled agriculture is being spread into regions where peasants are poor but, until now, have been self-sufficient in food. In the regions where industrial agriculture has been introduced through globalisation, higher costs are making it virtually impossible for small farmers to survive. The globalisation of non-sustainable industrial agriculture is literally evaporating the incomes of Third World farmers through a combination of devaluation of currencies, increase in costs of production and a collapse in commodity prices. Farmers everywhere are being paid a fraction of what they received for the same commodity a decade ago. The Canadian National Farmers Union put it like this in a report to the senate this year:

While the farmers growing cereal grains – wheat, oats, corn – earn negative returns and are pushed close to bankruptcy, the companies that make breakfast cereals reap huge profits. In 1998, cereal companies Kellogg's, Quaker Oats, and General Mills enjoyed return on equity rates of 56 per cent, 165 per cent and 222 per cent respectively. While a bushel of corn sold for less than $4, a bushel of corn flakes sold for $133 ... Maybe farmers are making too little because others are taking too much.

And a World Bank report has admitted that behind the polarisation of domestic consumer prices and world prices is the presence of large trading companies in international commodity markets.

While farmers earn less, consumers pay more. In India, food prices have doubled between 1999 and

2000. The consumption of food grains in rural areas has dropped by 12 per cent. Increased economic growth through global commerce is based on pseudo-surpluses. More food is being traded while the poor are consuming less. When growth increases poverty, when real production becomes a negative economy, and speculators are defined as 'wealth creators', something has gone wrong with the concepts and categories of wealth and wealth creation. Pushing the real production by nature and people into a negative economy implies that production of real goods and services is declining, creating deeper poverty for the millions who are not part of the dot.com route to instant wealth creation.

Recently, the McKinsey corporation said: 'American food giants recognise that Indian agribusiness has lots of room to grow, especially in food processing. India processes a minuscule 1 per cent of the food it grows compared with 70 per cent for the US ...' It is not that we Indians eat our food raw. Global consultants fail to see the 99 per cent food processing done by women at household level, or by the small cottage industry because it is not controlled by global agribusiness. Ninety-nine per cent of India's agroprocessing has been intentionally kept at the small level. Now, under the pressure of globalisation, things are changing. Pseudo-hygiene laws are being used to shut down local economies and small scale processing.

In August 1998, small scale local processing of edible

oil was banned in India through a 'packaging order' which made sale of open oil illegal and required all oil to be packaged in plastic or aluminium. This shut down tiny 'ghanis' or cold-pressed mills. It destroyed the market for our diverse oilseeds – mustard, linseed, sesame, groundnut, coconut. And the take-over of the edible oil industry has affected ten million livelihoods. The takeover of flour or 'atta' by packaged branded flour will cost 100 million livelihoods. And these millions are being pushed into new poverty. Also the forced use of packaging will increase the environmental burden of millions of tonnes of waste.

The globalisation of the food system is destroying the diversity of local food cultures and local food economies. A global monoculture is being forced on people by defining everything that is fresh, local and handmade as a health hazard. Human hands are being defined as the worst contaminants, and work for human hands is being outlawed, to be replaced by machines and chemicals bought from global corporations. These are not recipes for feeding the world, but stealing livelihoods from the poor to create markets for the powerful. People are being perceived as parasites, to be exterminated for the 'health' of the global economy. In the process new health and ecological hazards are being forced on Third World people through dumping of genetically engineered foods and other hazardous products.

Recently, because of a WTO ruling, India has been forced to remove restrictions on all imports. Among the unrestricted imports are carcasses and animal waste parts that create a threat to our culture and introduce public health hazards such as 'mad cow disease'. The US Centre for Disease Prevention in Atlanta has calculated that nearly eighty-one million cases of food borne illnesses occur in the US every year. Deaths from food poisoning have gone up more than four times due to deregulation. Most of these infections are caused by factory farmed meat. The US slaughters ninety-three million pigs, thirty-seven million cattle, two million calves, six million horses, goats and sheep and eight billion chickens and turkeys each year. Now the giant meat industry of the US wants to dump contaminated meat produced through violent and cruel methods on Indian consumers.

The waste of the rich is being dumped on the poor. The wealth of the poor is being violently appropriated through new and clever means like patents on biodiversity and indigenous knowledge. Patents and intellectual property rights are supposed to be granted for novel inventions. But patents are being claimed for rice varieties such as the basmati, or pesticides derived from the neem which our mothers and grandmothers have been using. Rice Tec, a US based company has been granted patent no. 5,663,484 for basmati rice lines and grains. Basmati, neem, pepper, bitter gourd, turmeric, every aspect of the innovation embodied in our indigenous food and medicinal systems is now being pirated and patented. The knowledge of the poor is being converted into the property of global corporations, creating a situation where the poor will have to pay for the seeds and medicines they have evolved and have used to meet their own needs for nutrition and healthcare.

Such false claims to creation are now the global norm, with the Trade Related Intellectual Property Rights Agreement of the World Trade Organisation forcing countries to introduce regimes that allow patenting of life forms and indigenous knowledge. Instead of recognising that commercial interests build on nature and on the contribution of other cultures, global law has enshrined the patriarchal myth of creation to create new property rights to life forms just as colonialism used the myth of discovery as the basis of the takeover of the land of others as colonies.

Humans do not create life when they manipulate it. Rice Tec's claim that it has made 'an instant invention of a novel rice line', or Roslin Institute's claim that Ian Wilmut 'created' Dolly denies the creativity of nature, the self-organisational capacity of life forms, and the prior innovations of Third World communities. Patents and intellectual property rights are supposed to prevent piracy. Instead they are becoming the instruments of pirating the common traditional knowledge from the poor of the Third World and making it the exclusive 'property' of western scientists and corporations.

When patents are granted for seeds and plants, as in the case of basmati, theft is defined as creation, and saving and sharing seed is defined as theft of intellectual property. Corporations which have broad patents on crops such as cotton, soya beans or mustard are suing farmers for seed saving and hiring detective agencies to find out if farmers have saved seed or shared it with neighbours. The recent announcement that Monsanto is giving away the rice genome for free is misleading, because Monsanto has never made a commitment that it will never patent rice varieties or any other crop varieties. Sharing and exchange, the basis of our humanity and of our ecological survival have been redefined as a crime. This makes us all poor. Nature has given us abundance. Women's indigenous knowledge of biodiversity, agriculture and nutrition has built on that abundance to create more from less, to create growth through sharing.

The poor are pushed into deeper poverty by making them pay for what was theirs. Even the rich are poorer because their profits are based on theft and on the use of coercion and violence. This is not wealth creation but plunder. Sustainability requires the protection of all species and all people and the recognition that diverse species and diverse people play an essential role in maintaining ecological processes. Pollinators are critical to the fertilisation and generation of plants. Biodiversity in fields provides vegetables, fodder, medicine and protection to the soil from water and wind erosion. As humans travel further down the road to non-sustainability, they become intolerant of other species and blind to their vital role in our survival.

In 1992, when Indian farmers destroyed Cargill's seed plant in Bellary, Karnataka, to protest against seed failure, the Cargill chief executive stated, 'We bring Indian farmers smart technologies which prevent bees from usurping the pollen'. When I was participating in the United Nations Biosafety Negotiations, Monsanto circulated literature to defend its herbicide resistant Roundup ready-crops on the grounds that they prevent 'weeds from stealing the sunshine'. But what Monsanto calls weeds are the green fields that provide vitamin A rice and prevent blindness in children and anaemia in women.

A worldview that defines pollination as 'theft by bees' and claims biodiversity 'steals' sunshine is a worldview which itself aims at stealing nature's harvest by replacing open, pollinated varieties with hybrids and sterile seeds, and destroying biodiverse flora with herbicides such as Roundup. The threat posed to the Monarch butterfly by genetically engineered crops is just one example of the ecological poverty created by the new biotechnologies. As butterflies and bees disappear, production is undermined. As biodiversity disappears, with it go sources of nutrition and food. When giant corporations view small peasants and bees as thieves and through trade rules and new technologies seek the right to exterminate them, humanity has reached a dangerous threshold. The imperative to stamp out the smallest insect, the smallest plant, the smallest peasant comes from a deep fear – the fear of everything that is alive and free. And this deep insecurity and fear is unleashing the violence against all people and all species.

The global free trade economy has become a threat to sustainability and the very survival of the poor and other species is at stake not just as a side-effect or as an exception but in a systemic way through a restructuring of our worldview at the most fundamental level. Sustainability, sharing and survival are being economically outlawed in the name of market competitiveness and market efficiency.

The world can be fed only by feeding all beings that make the world. In giving food to other beings and species we maintain conditions for our own food security. In feeding earthworms we feed ourselves. In feeding cows, we feed the soil, and in providing food for the soil, we provide food for humans. This worldview of abundance is based on sharing and on a deep awareness of humans as members of the Earth family. This awareness that in impoverishing other beings, we impoverish ourselves and in nourishing other beings, we nourish ourselves is the real basis of sustainability.

The sustainability challenge for the new millennium

is whether global economic man can move out of the worldview based on fear and scarcity, monocultures and monopolies, appropriation and dispossession and shift to a view based on abundance and sharing, diversity and decentralisation, and respect and dignity for all beings. Sustainability demands that we move out of the economic trap that is leaving no space for other species and other people. Economic globalisation has become a war against nature and the poor. But the rules of globalisation are not God-given. They can be changed. They must be changed. We must bring this war to an end.

Since Seattle, a frequently used phrase has been the need for a rule-based system. Globalisation is the rule of commerce and it has elevated Wall Street to be the only source of value. As a result things that should have high worth – nature, culture, the future – are being devalued and destroyed. The rules of globalisation are undermining the rules of justice and sustainability, of compassion and sharing. We have to move from market totalitarianism to an Earth democracy. We can survive as a species only if we live by the rules of the biosphere. The biosphere has enough for everyone's needs if the global economy respects the limits set by sustainability and justice. As Gandhi had reminded us: 'The earth has enough for everyone's needs, but not for some people's greed'.

6

A Royal View

HRH The Prince of Wales

Like millions of other people around the world I was fascinated to hear five eminent speakers share with us their thoughts hopes and fears about sustainable development. All five of those contributions have been immensely thoughtful and challenging. There have been clear differences of opinion and of emphasis between the speakers but there have also been some important common themes, both implicit and explicit. One of those themes has been the suggestion that sustainable development is a matter of 'enlightened self-interest'. Two of the speakers used this phrase and I don't believe that the other three would dissent from it, and nor would I.

Self-interest is a powerful motivating force for all of us, and if we can somehow convince ourselves that sustainable development is in all our interests then we will have taken a valuable first step towards achieving it. But self-interest comes in many competing guises – not all of which, I fear, are likely to lead in the right direction for very long, nor to embrace the manifold needs of future generations. We will need to dig rather deeper to find the inspiration, sense of urgency and moral purpose required to confront the hard choices which face us on the long road to sustainable development. So, although it seems to have become deeply unfashionable to talk about the spiritual dimension of our existence, that is what I propose to do.

The idea that there is a sacred trust between mankind and our Creator, under which we accept a duty of stewardship for the earth, has been an important feature of most religious and spiritual thought throughout the ages. Even those whose beliefs have not included the existence of a Creator have, nevertheless, adopted a similar position on moral and ethical grounds. It is only recently that this guiding principle has become smothered by almost impenetrable layers of scientific rationalism. If we are to achieve genuinely sustainable development we will first have to rediscover, or re-acknowledge, a sense of the sacred in our dealings with the natural world, and with each other. If literally nothing is held sacred any more – because it is considered synonymous with superstition or in some other way 'irrational' — what is there to prevent us from treating our entire world as some 'great laboratory of life' with potentially disastrous long-term consequences?

Fundamentally, an understanding of the sacred helps us to acknowledge that there are bounds of balance, order and harmony in the natural world which set limits to our ambitions, and define the parameters of sustainable development. In some cases nature's limits are well understood at the rational, scientific level. As a simple example, we know that trying to graze too many sheep on a hillside will, sooner or later, be counterproductive for the sheep, the hillside, or both. More widely we understand that the overuse of insecticides or antibiotics leads to problems of resistance. And we are beginning to comprehend the full, awful consequences of pumping too much carbon dioxide into the earth's atmosphere. Yet the actions being taken to halt the damage known to be caused by exceeding nature's limits in these and other ways are insufficient to ensure a sustainable outcome. In other areas, such as the artificial and uncontained transfer of genes between species of plants and animals, the lack of hard, scientific evidence of harmful consequences is regarded in many quarters as sufficient reason to allow such developments to proceed.

The idea of taking a precautionary approach, in this and many other potentially damaging situations, receives overwhelming public support, but still faces a degree of official opposition, as if admitting the possibility of doubt was a sign of weakness or even of a wish to halt 'progress'. On the contrary, I believe it to be a sign of strength and of wisdom. It seems that when we do have scientific evidence that we are damaging our environment we aren't doing enough to put things right, and when we don't have that evidence we are prone to do nothing at all, regardless of the risks.

Part of the problem is the prevailing approach that seeks to reduce the natural world, including ourselves, to the level of nothing more than a mechanical process. For whilst the natural theologians of the eighteenth and nineteenth centuries, like Thomas Morgan, referred to the perfect unity, order, wisdom and design of the natural world, scientists like Bertrand Russell rejected this idea as rubbish. 'I think the universe', he wrote, 'is all spots and jumps without unity and without continuity, without coherence or orderliness'. Sir Julian Huxley wrote in *Creation: a Modern Synthesis* that 'modern science must rule out special creation or divine guidance.' But why?

Professor Alan Linton of Bristol University wrote, 'evolution is a manmade theory to explain the origin and continuance of life on this planet without reference to a Creator.' It is because of our inability or refusal to accept the existence of a guiding hand that nature has come to be regarded as a system that can be engineered for our own convenience or as a nuisance to be evaded and manipulated, and in which anything that happens can be fixed by technology and human ingenuity. Fritz Schumacher recognised the inherent dangers in this approach when he said that 'there are two sciences – the science of manipulation and the science of understanding.'

In this technology-driven age it is all too easy for us to forget that mankind is a part of nature and not apart from it. And that this is why we should seek to work with the grain of nature in everything we do, for the natural world is, as the economist Herman Daly puts it, 'the envelope that contains, sustains and provisions the economy, not the other way round.' So which argument will win – the living world as one, or, the world made up of random parts, the product of mere chance, thereby providing the justification for any kind of development? This, to my mind, lies at the heart of what we call sustainable development. We need, therefore, to rediscover a reference for the natural world, irrespective of its usefulness to ourselves – to become more aware in Philip Sherrard's words of 'the relationship of interdependence, interpenetration and reciprocity between God, Man and Creation.'

Above all, we should show greater respect for the genius of nature's designs, rigorously tested and refined over millions of years. This means being careful to use science to understand how nature works, not to change what nature is, as we do when genetic manipulation seeks to transform a process of biological evolution into something altogether different. The idea that the different parts of the natural world are connected through an intricate system of checks and balances which we disturb at our peril is all too easily dismissed as no longer relevant.

In an age when we are told that science has all the answers, what chance is there for working with the grain of nature? As an example of working with the grain of nature, I happen to believe that if a fraction of the money currently being invested in developing genetically manipulated crops were applied to understanding and improving traditional systems of agriculture, which have stood the all-important test of time, the results would be remarkable. There is already plenty of evidence of just what can be achieved through applying more knowledge and fewer chemicals to diverse cropping systems. These are genuinely sustainable methods and they are far removed from the approaches based on monoculture which lend themselves to large-scale commercial exploitation, and which Vandana Shiva has condemned so persuasively and so convincingly. Our most eminent scientists accept that there is still a vast amount that we don't know about our world and the life forms that inhabit it. As Sir Martin Rees, the Astronomer Royal, points out, it is complexity that makes things hard to understand, not size. In a comment that only an astronomer could make, he describes a butterfly as a more daunting intellectual challenge than the cosmos!

Others, like Rachel Carson, have eloquently reminded us that we don't know how to make a single blade of grass. And St Matthew, in his wisdom, emphasised that not even Solomon in all his glory was arrayed as the lilies of the field. Faced with such unknowns it is hard not to feel a sense of humility, wonder and awe about our place in the natural order. And to feel this at all stems from that inner heart-felt reason which sometimes, despite ourselves, is telling us that we are intimately bound up in the mysteries of life and that we don't have all the answers. Perhaps even that we don't have to have all the answers before knowing what we should do in certain circumstances. As Blaise Pascal wrote in the seventeenth century, 'it is the heart that experiences God, not the reason.'

Do you not feel that, buried deep within each and every one of us, there is an instinctive, heart-felt awareness that provides – if we will allow it to – the most reliable guide as to whether or not our actions are really in the long-term interests of our planet and all the life it supports? This awareness, this wisdom of the heart, maybe no more than a faint memory of a distant harmony, rustling like a breeze through the leaves, yet sufficient to remind us that the earth is unique and that we have a duty to care for it. Wisdom, empathy and compassion have no place in the empirical world yet traditional wisdoms would ask 'without them are we truly human?' It was Socrates who, when asked for his definition of wisdom, gave as his conclusion, 'knowing that you don't know'.

In suggesting that we will need to listen rather more to the common sense emanating from our hearts if we are to achieve sustainable development, I'm not suggesting that information gained through scientific investigation is anything other than essential. Far from it. But I believe that we need to restore the balance between the heart-felt reason of instinctive wisdom and the rational insights of scientific analysis. Neither is much use on its own. It is only by employing both the intuitive and the rational halves of our own nature – our hearts and our minds – that we will live up to the sacred trust that has been placed in us by our Creator – or our 'Sustainer', as ancient wisdom referred to the Creator. Gro Harlem Brundtland reminded us that sustainable development is not just about the natural world, but about people too. This applies whether we are looking at the vast numbers who lack sufficient food or access to clean water, but also those living in poverty and without work. While there is no doubt that globalisation has brought advantages, it brings dangers too. Without the humility and humanity expressed by the notion of the 'connected economy' – an economy which acknowledges the social and environmental context within which it operates – there is the risk that the poorest and the weakest will not only see very little benefit but, worse, they may find that their livelihoods and cultures have been lost.

If we are serious about sustainable development then we must also remember that the lessons of history are particularly relevant when we start to look further ahead. In an age when it often seems that nothing can properly be regarded as important unless it can be described as 'modern', it is highly dangerous to talk about the lessons of the past. And are those lessons ever taught or understood adequately in an age when to pass on a body of acquired knowledge of this kind is often considered prejudicial to 'progress'? Our descendants will have scientific and technological expertise beyond our imagining, but will they have the insight or the self-control to use this wisely, having learned both from our successes and our failures?

They won't unless there are increased efforts to develop an approach to education which balances the rational with the intuitive. Without this truly sustainable development is doomed. It will merely become a hollow-sounding mantra that is repeated *ad nauseam* in order to make us all feel better. Surely, therefore, we need to look towards the creation of greater balance in the way we educate people so that the practical and intuitive wisdom of the past can be blended with the appropriate technology and knowledge of the present to produce the type of practitioner who is acutely aware of both the visible and invisible worlds that inform the entire cosmos. The future will need people who understand that sustainable development is not merely about a series of technical fixes, about redesigning humanity or re-engineering nature in an extension of globalised industrialisation – but about a re-connection with nature and a profound understanding of the concepts of care that underpin long-term stewardship.

Only by rediscovering the essential unity and order of the living and spiritual world – as in the case of organic agriculture or integrated medicine or in the way we build – and by bridging the destructive chasm between cynical secularism and the timelessness of traditional religion, will we avoid the disintegration of our overall environment. Above all, I don't want to see the day when we are rounded upon by our grandchildren and asked accusingly why we didn't listen more carefully to the wisdom of our hearts as well as to the rational analysis of our heads; why we didn't pay more attention to the preservation of biodiversity and traditional communities or think more clearly about our role as stewards of creation? Taking a cautious approach or achieving balance in life is never as much fun as the alternatives, but that is what sustainable development is all about.

Conclusion

James Naughtie: The phrase 'the living world as one' has been the objective of the five different approaches that we've heard in this year's Reith lectures. So what are the hard choices that need to be made and will they be made? What are the dangers of that becoming a piece of political fashion rather than an engine of change in decision-making?

Chris Patten: Considerable. I start with good old St Matthew and the lilies which I think he went on to say 'neither spin nor do they weave', which is of course true. And life is about value as well as price. Not that there has been all that much change in philosophy or approach in the recognition of value over the last few years, even if the language has changed. That may have happened at the margins but not very centrally. Even though policies have, in a strictly environmental sense, often changed, to some extent I think the paradox is that in other areas we've gone backwards. One of the problems that we face today is that globalisation hasn't been accompanied by the rich countries accepting that there is a poor agenda, so that we've seen a fall in development assistance to poor countries, with a really substantial impact on the environment. Some things have gone backwards rather than progressed.

James Naughtie: Vandana Shiva, you used the word 'smug' while talking about globalisation. The issue is whether 'language' to some degree has become a cover for doing nothing?

Vandana Shiva: It's not just a cover for doing nothing – it's a cover for basically doing unjust acts and engaging in non-sustainable processes. The idea that rules written by a group of commerce officials are irreversible means that we can never correct our errors. These are not God-given, they are not natural phenomena. The rules of commerce and free trade and globalisation are basically rules human beings got together and wrote. There are other rules human beings wrote, like the climate change treaty, like the convention on biological diversity, which are being marginalised. It is time to bring the rules that protect people and the planet to the core of decision-making.

James Naughtie: So the question for businessmen is whether you can deliver the sorts of changes which are needed. Will it happen?

John Browne: I think it will, provided the right time scales are thought through and that rhetoric doesn't overtake the reality of what has to happen on the ground. We have to be authentic in what we say we're going to do – lay it out and then do it and do it again and again. And sometimes the achievements are smaller than people would expect. And therefore they always beg the second question which is, well do more.

James Naughtie: Some people might say that that kind of authenticity is caution, is it?

John Browne: No, it's not caution. It's practicality. And it takes more than ten seconds to figure out what to do – how to, for example, capture CO_2 and re-inject it into deep reservoirs. How to create very minimal disruption to the environment as necessary things are happening – whether that is the discovery of hydrocarbons or the building of homes. These things take time. It's not to say that people are taking all the time. They just have to move as fast as they can and it's not as fast as the words can be spoken.

James Naughtie: But when you go the Amazonian rain forests, Tom Lovejoy, which you do all the time, do you sense that that process with governments and with businesses is happening fast enough? You talk about a spasm of extinction greater than any we have known since the age of the dinosaurs – the polar ice caps starting to melt in twenty years – pretty alarming stuff. Do you think that the thinking-through process is happening at the right pace?

Tom Lovejoy: There are good signs all over the place but they are still insufficient to the challenge in front of us. The reason that I would be optimistic is that when I see humanity confronted with challenges, I often see great creativity arising in response to it and that's exactly the kind of thing we need to be dealing with now.

James Naughtie: What does that creativity mean as you look at the tragic cost of poor health across the developing world?

Gro Harlem Brundtland: The reduction in attention to development co-operation and the redistribution of funds in the global economy – the fact that that has been sliding back is a tragedy. In the face of all the necessary needs for change it still has happened. However, what we also see now is that civil society – private foundations – are coming forward to fill part of the gap. Not that that is the only answer, but it may add to the awareness in many societies. Only based on shared values can we move towards sustainability.

Chris Patten: It is quite extraordinary that during the

1990s, when our rhetoric about internationalisation had become more sustained, that we saw a fall in the amount of assistance which rich countries gave to poor countries. It is not enough to say that is made good by private investment. Private investment does not go to the poorest and it does not go to the poorest countries. And the figures of those affected are an affront to our common humanity and they also lead to the prospect of insecurity – environmental and political insecurity. It is terribly important to re-establish the moral and the practical, the expedient case in relation to the environment, in relation to our political stability of good old-fashioned development assistance – spending money on people, on their health, on their education as well as on their environment.

Vandana Shiva: Part of the problem is that there are new ways being found of draining the last resources of the poor – and no matter how much development assistance is given, even if it's brought back to the older levels – if in the meantime you have patents on seeds, plants and medicine, which will increase the debt burden of the Third World countries tenfold just to pay royalties for knowledge and biodiversity that was theirs in the first place. You've got a mechanism for creating poverty.

James Naughtie: How do you challenge that mechanism politically?

Vandana Shiva: You need to challenge the models of intellectual property rights that have been enshrined into the World Trade Organisation. These are implemented through the trade-related intellectual property which all Third World governments, all of Africa, India, Central America, say need to be re-written. These laws are not suitable to govern a world for justice and sustainability. We need to revise those norms.

James Naughtie: Tom Lovejoy, you have talked about sustainable development as a theory and as a way of life for a very long time. Working with the World Bank presently, which is seen by many people as an agent of these practices which is making things worse not better, how can you say that it isn't?

Tom Lovejoy: The World Bank is sort of a mix like any government, any country – there are a lot of good things and there are a lot of 'old-fashioned' things that go on. However, I do have an uncomfortable feeling about the wave of prosperity that we've had in the United States in particular – it doesn't seem to be accompanied by greater generosity in overseas assistance, rather it's leading to inward-looking tendencies and more consumption instead of taking advantage of it to do good.

James Naughtie: Do you think that prosperity means that the sense of urgency is dulled?

John Browne: It is a matter of understanding where the power actually lies. The reality is that however business is done in the world, it is inter-connected. Trade has always been around and it remains the vital fundamental of business. So to say that everything could be done inside a country and that you're fine and everyone else isn't, is to sign a very bad certificate for the future. The connectivity of the world that we now have, where people can understand what's going on anywhere at any time simply makes it more difficult to sustain that position.

James Naughtie: The Commission in Brussels could be accused by outsiders as being part of a great lumbering machine that acknowledges that things cannot be done in every country. To many outsiders it seems to have failed in vital areas like agriculture. It is seen as wasteful and inefficient. Is it?

Chris Patten: Some of its manifestations as less than desirable. But I want to make a point about international organisations, whether the European Union or the WTO or the World Bank. We all know that the nation state remains the basic political unit, but we also know that everybody recognises, because of global trends, that more has to be determined on a regional, international, global level, so we set up these organisations which, alas, haven't yet found a way of command-

ing the loyalty which people feel towards national institutions. In defence of the World Bank, it has probably
done more than any other global organisation to recognise the new world we're living in, to recognise the
importance of the environment and of social issues. The
consequence of the recent demonstrations against the
World Bank is that the World Bank will get fewer
resources to spend in poor countries because of being
discredited in Washington bang next door to Capitol
Hill. This is the awful paradox. Here is an organisation
which reflects the importance of transfers from rich to
poor, which reflects the importance of having international rules. The World Bank which is on the side of
the poor has been extremely unfairly criticised.

Vandana Shiva: When the World Bank and IMF go
for replenishments – they lay out figures and say that for
every dollar they put into poor countries they make
three dollars for the rich countries and that's the justification which keeps them running. Being an environmental researcher and campaigner has brought me
against project aid after project aid from the World
Bank, which has devastated our people and our ecosystems. The entire conversion of our rich forest bio-
diveristy into eucalyptus monoculture is financed by the
Bank; the destruction of the mangroves along our coasts
leading to huge cyclone damage, salinity for coastal
areas, was financed by the Bank for industrial shrimp

farming; the erosion of our genetic diversity in agriculture was financed by the Bank for the green revolution – the list is absolutely endless. If the World Bank is an issue for northern environmentalists and northern campaigners, it is because movements of hundreds and thousands of tribals and peasants in the Third World have talked about the threat to their very survival.

James Naughtie: If we accept that globalisation in some form is here and is going to continue – what changes are needed to encourage and manage the global economy to avoid that kind of disaster?

Vandana Shiva: When it is made to look like it is the first time we are doing international trade I keep thinking of all the pepper from India that brought the British and got Columbus sailing in the wrong direction, claiming he had discovered North America. We have had international trade before. We have had rules of international trade before. We have also had free trade rules before which led to the Bengal famine of 1942. We need to allow countries to restrict exports and imports if the environment, public health or livelihood protection requires it. We will have to put that freedom of countries back on the agenda, because on it is based the freedom of people.

James Naughtie: Slum clearance in the nineteenth

century happened when it was in the interests of society to stop it developing, to stop disease spreading. Is that the kind of incentive that is going to produce change?

Gro Harlem Brundtland: I hope so. It is one strong argument about why we are in this together. European countries historically dealt with what was next door – the things they saw and understood – and they made changes in the policy directions which improved the quality of life and the quality of societies. But they didn't go far enough to look at it around the globe and to see the same problem far away in the colonial parts.

James Naughtie: At one point in our history governments tended to look on the developing world, on health, as a luxury that came after basic economic development. If you produce better health then you will get poverty down. Is it the idea that the governments understand and are willing to act upon?

Gro Harlem Brundtland: Increasingly, I see that happening. Several governments are now aware that it is not wise to let human capital lessen and sink into poverty instead of, for instance, giving all children vaccines. Thirty million children don't get vaccinated with basic, simple technologies that all of us in our countries take for granted. Three million die because they don't get those quite cheap vaccines at the time in life when they need it. Families keep getting more children. Families feel that they cannot depend on their children growing up, and it adds to the total burden of people feeling incapacitated and disempowered. Why are we not able to vaccinate every child? Why is that not an obligation to all of us as it is in our own countries? We wouldn't dream of not being able to vaccinate all our own children wherever they live.

James Naughtie: Human security in the United States is as important now as national security. Do you think people believe that or have yet understood it, assuming that it's true?

Gro Harlem Brundtland: There is an on-going debate which can be brought forward about that issue.

Chris Patten: The focus in the United States is on investing in spectacular out-of-space technology in order to protect the United States from the insecurity of the world in the twenty-first century. Whether or not that is a sensible approach, for most of us geography renders that simply impossible, and the only way you can actually deal with insecurity is by trying to invest in peoples' prosperity and in their stability. It is actually in our interest to invest in peoples' health. The Asian Development Bank has pointed out that one of the reasons for East Asia's spectacular success was land reform, was believing in leaving business to businessmen, but was also investing in people, in their basic health and basic education. And the extraordinary improvements in literacy rates, in child mortality statistics and so on in East Asia was one of the reasons for economic take-off there. Issues about vaccines and ill health in developing countries, which is, of course, related to environmental issues, reflect on the rich countries' agenda. Take pharmaceutical companies – there is no difficulty in getting pharmaceutical companies to invest in the ailments of the rich, in baldness and impotence, in their heart disease – but encourage them to invest in a vaccine against malaria and you'll find only eighty million a year is being spent on that. But malaria kills two and a half million people every year.

James Naughtie: How do you get companies to understand the interests in that kind of investment? To many of them it is less obviously a good investment than what they do at the moment?

John Browne: It is the case, not just in pharmaceuticals but in a lot of activity, where the full value of the activity has to be exposed very transparently.

James Naughtie: By who?

John Browne: By both the business people and the

government. There's always a sharing of rent – in one way or another – between government and a business. Many people think business just comes in, does something and leaves. In my business that is the last thing we can do. We are actually there for hundreds of years and therefore we must strike a balance of who gets what part of the rent distribution. Because when you think of all the things involved, then you'll get the equation right.

Chris Patten: They invest in baldness rather than malaria because they think there is money in that. Governments can actually help to shape the market by making the real costs of things apparent – the externalities as economists call them – and by offering inducements. The rich governments should be giving a guarantee to pay for each vaccine which is used against malaria, which will then stimulate the private sector to do the research and development of the drug which is necessary.

John Browne: The tools and techniques are well-known. They're to do with taxation and market instruments and they really do work. If you take the case of the environment, you could pass thousands of regulations concerned with reducing carbon dioxide emissions. But actually if you just get to trade permits you have an extraordinary way of clearing the market, letting people get on with things and actually getting a result.

James Naughtie: Tom, what do you want to see?

Tom Lovejoy: In the short-term – a corporation that is facing some activity they want to get into, which will release CO_2 paying for a CO_2 offset elsewhere in the world – wherever that market may be.

James Naughtie: Are we talking about punitive taxes?

John Browne: No, we're talking about a balance of incentives. There is always a carrot, and there is always the stick – there must be that. There must also be enforcement and transparency.

James Naughtie: What do governments and societies do about businesses which aren't enlightened, and which do not behave appropriately?

John Browne: No business wants to have a free-loader around – someone who takes advantage of the system. In practical terms, there's a huge demand for transparency, to say what you're going to do, and then report against what you have said so that keeps going well. Also, the introduction of market-based mechanisms where people who break the rules have to pay a tremendous amount of money. And enforcement. That is important since it is the contract with society that is expressed by the role of government here as the enforcer.

James Naughtie: Can a mixture of market mechanisms and enforcement produce the desired effect?

Vandana Shiva: The part that we constantly forget is people in society. It is not just government acting through business and regulations on business, but governments empowering, defending the rights of people, ensuring small farmers are able to stay on land, practice organic farming, that public health is a universal right for all, that food access and entitlements is a global right. The defence of the rights of people is the biggest obligation of governments and we can't always mediate those rights via the market and by purchasing power because a large number of the poor who do not have purchasing power cannot get their entitlements through the market, and it is the exclusion of those rights and the exclusion of the government functions in the defence of those rights that has been the big sacrifice in globalisation. We need to reintroduce that debate.

Gro Harlem Brundtland: It is difficult to find the exact balance. The world is negotiating in different areas, not only in commerce, but on biodiversity, on climate convention, and looking for solutions which can work across the board. That process has to continue, but one has to take into greater account and take into the balance more of what is said than that which has been the case until now. Some of the rich countries who are dominating negotiations have had the ability to make definitions about how they take care of all parts of their societies, and then they negotiate and have a stronger negotiating power than smaller countries or poorer countries, so the balance is not right.

James Naughtie: You said that the world should learn to look at itself through the eyes of the poor. Do you really believe in a world of vast transfers of money across borders, enormous explosions of wealth in the developed world – that that is happening or will happen?

Gro Harlem Brundtland: It is happening and our ability in our democracies to take care of those who need to be taken care of with their human rights, with their place in society, that has to be increased. But climate convention and the permits and the exchange of rights or duties with regard to emission of CO_2, these need further discussion.

James Naughtie: What is the importance of government being inclusive, perhaps more outward-looking than it's been in the western world in the past, as a means of meeting that challenge. Is that happening?

Chris Patten: Governments and traditional political structures have not yet found a way of coping with entering a proper and comprehensive dialogue with present manifestations of civil society which are not always candidly very democratic. They are sometimes democratic, but not always. It is a very curious world that we live in – in which NGOs are often very much better resourced, for example, than UN bodies or UN institutions. You see it in the human rights and environmental fields. And I don't think one should always begin from the assumption that the democratically elected government or the international organisation, which is very often a combination of the political efforts of democratically elected governments, is wrong and the NGOs are right. I think we have to develop a more open dialogue between them if we want to have change in society and changes in political attitudes.

James Naughtie: Tom Lovejoy, you suggested we have some biodiverse areas around the world, Los Angeles, somewhere in South America, somewhere in the Indian sub-continent, a startling thought. Most governments would say, lovely idea, great to hear it in a Reith lecture, but it will never happen. Can something like that occur and is that the kind of spark without which this just remains academic talk?

Tom Lovejoy: Some of it is happening – a surprising amount is happening – such as a middle American biological corridor from Mexico all the way to Colombia.

It is, of course, not enough. The really important thing is what happens in particular places. For example – there is no solution to the Amazon problem until the twenty million people living there have an adequate quality of life, and that is what we have to join all the different sectors together to address.

James Naughtie: You regularly take American senators and congressmen down to the Amazon and say here is the situation – here is what we have to tackle. How do you cope with the senator's reaction who says, I see the enormity of what you point out to me, but back home they are not going to give up their car?

Tom Lovejoy: The interesting thing is that the senators I have taken down are very good about all of this – it's the ones who haven't gone I worry about. And that's not just a problem of the particular elected officials, although there is always a big lag-time between who is holding office and public opinion. Public opinion is not strong enough in the United States yet, they don't get the sense of urgency.

Chris Patten: It has always been the most difficult task of political democratic leadership to convince people that something which seems to be painful or involving sacrifice in the short-term is actually best for them in the medium- or long-term, and the excitement of democratic politics is that it should enable you to mobilise opinion in that way.

James Naughtie: You are referring to leadership?

Chris Patten: It's what we call leadership rather than focus groups – rather than going to a focus group to discover not just what you want to say but how to say it.

John Browne: The tools and techniques are available. Governments do have to take a real position of policy in leadership in amongst all this noise and debate. To opt out is really to give a very strange result to this where the voice of the few will direct the actions of the many and that is a problem.

James Naughtie: The Prince of Wales spoke passionately about the need to understand how people and progress are different sides of the same coin, how the earth is still a sacred trust – wherever you come from on the religious or moral spectrum. How do we put together the enormity of such thoughts with the practical business of day-to-day life – in politics, in business, in organisations which are trying to tackle seemingly insoluble problems of health. What do you do in the next five years?

Gro Harlem Brundtland: At a recent summit in

Nigeria twenty African leaders came together for two days, and discussed in great detail the problem of malaria. On that continent three hundred million people are sick every year and it undermines the future, the economic potential, the human potential and it creates insecurity for life. If government leaders don't deal with basic human concerns like this – and it's linked to the environment – there is no way forward. If they don't focus on these issues as basic social and environmental concerns, how can they lead their countries into the future? We see ourselves as supporting those kinds of actions. In practical terms – getting bed nets to every African child in every country where their life is threatened by malaria.

James Naughtie: John Browne, what is your action plan?

John Browne: You can break it down into a programme. The most important thing is for the leadership of any commercial enterprise, the leadership itself needs to be educated and experienced. People must see with their own eyes what is actually going on in Bombay, Azerbaijan, Algeria. It doesn't matter where. You have to go to see and you must talk to people and you need to understand what it means and therefore an experienced presence is critical. Then, deciding what to do, saying what you're going to do and reporting against it and making it part of everyday life. This is not something which is separate and apart from making money, or educating – or developing your staff. It is one and the same thing. It's part of everyday experience. How do we clean up the water a little bit? How do we make sure less CO_2 is released? How can we develop one more person to give them an idea of what the promise of the future is? These things are day-to-day, but they are all to do with delivering a business result.

James Naughtie: Tom Lovejoy, you gave an alarming picture of the kinds of disasters that might lie around the corner if we don't get this right. In practical terms, how do we get it right?

Tom Lovejoy: It breaks down into almost two distinct but related issues – one is climate change. We simply can't allow CO_2 to accumulate to two, three, even more, times on our pre-industrial levels, and things can be done in terms of carbon trading and new technologies, such as hydrogen fuel cells. The other issue really comes down to biodiveristy and what happens in landscapes.

James Naughtie: Many people are arguing that there is a willingness to accept some short-term pain given the enormity of the issues that we face. Do you believe that's true?

Tom Lovejoy: It often turns out that the pain is less than people think.

James Naughtie: Vandana Shiva, looking ahead what are the practical things that you want to see to move towards the a sustained world?

Vandana Shiva: Most immediately what I work towards and what I'd like to see is the possibility that small farms in every country, north and south, rich and poor, are able to survive into the future with sustainable methods, that that becomes a reality. To make that reality happen we will need to change the rules of trade, national agricultural policies, to rewrite the agreement on agriculture in the WTO, centre more on sustainability and small farm survival. I want to see farmers everywhere have the inviolable right to save seed because seed is sacred. It's their duty to save it and that would mean changes in the intellectual property rights laws worldwide, to exempt and exclude life forms from patentability because life is sacred. It's not a human engineered invention. It is the very symbol and embodiment of creation and its continuity.

James Naughtie: Do you see that threatened by the genetically modified organisms?

Vandana Shiva: We now have more than enough

evidence that genetic engineering is not an imperative because without it people will not starve. Organic production increases food production many fold. It sustains biodiversity, protects the earth, and protects all farmers while bringing us good food. It is time that at least 50 per cent of the world's money was put into research on organic methods and improvement of indigenous methods rather than this blind investment only in genetic engineering whose hazards are known, whose counter-productivity is now established and which increases monopoly controls which we can't afford.

James Naughtie: How do you succeed in this task to make a difference?

Chris Patten: You have to believe that people are capable of being and doing better. The words reverence, awe and value are all important and should be much more part of our political debate. One has to challenge people with the facts, for example, that today we spend eleven billion Euros in Europe on ice cream which is about twice what it would cost to provide access to clean drinking water for people in poor countries. I think those sort of moral affronts are things that people have to be challenged with to lift their eyes beyond the GDP figures to a rather more important horizon.

James Naughtie: Perhaps we should all meet again in ten years or so and see how far we have got. Thank you very much to all our Reith lecturers.

The Public Debate

What is and is not acceptable for the health of the planet and the wellbeing of its people – and who should decide? The Reith 2000 lecturers grappled with the difficult issues surrounding the goal of sustainable development. This section displays public opinion on this issue. Comments have been selected from the BBC website published concurrently with the lecture series and from the debates which followed each lecture.

Chris Patten – Questions and Answers

Tim O'Riordan, University of East Anglia in Norwich: I'd like to push further on the issue of governance for sustainability. Throughout these lectures one of the common strands is that an earth, which is limited, can only handle so many people – it can handle more people if they consume less and very many less people if they consume more. Democracy has pushed people to wanting to consume more, and if they wished to have that level of consumption and democracies have to deliver, then governments have to do something about standing in the way. Now, do you believe that we need a different form of government, which is more partnership based, linking people, not just through civil society but to business, and across space and time in a much more complex way than traditional state and international structures are right now?

Chris Patten: There's a sense in which good government and democratic government in the past helped to produce our problems today. From the later years of the nineteenth century onwards, as governments became more participative, they reflected the aspirations of ordinary people and it can't be any coincidence that those aspirations included a decent sewage system. Those aspirations included literacy, better healthcare and so on. And what was the result of that? The result of that is something that we don't often talk about as an example of good governance, death control. And it's death control in the last century which ensured that the population of the world trebled and the biggest impact on our environment, the biggest challenge to sustainable development is that huge increase in population in the last century and in particular the huge increase in our urban populations — a growing problem in Asia today. You can argue from that that it would have been better if we'd had lousy authoritarian governments which didn't take account of people's aspirations for living longer, for living healthier – that would be the sort of extraordinary eco-fascist argument which one sometimes hears at the wildest extremes, but no sensible person would support that. The challenge for democracies is to convince people in the developed countries that success isn't just about appetites – that success isn't just about extending appetites. Democracies are more likely to be able to take that trick than authoritarian governments. There are some examples of a more authoritarian style which has also produced long-term decisions in the interests of the environment. To be fair to Mr Lee Kuan Yew's Singapore – it is true of Singapore. But Singapore is not a paradigm for Asia nor a paradigm for the whole world. Democratic leaders have to recognise, and some to their credit have done, that political success isn't just about getting through the next four or five years. If democratic leaders can't do it nobody else is going to be able to do it.

Raj Thamotheram, corporate social responsibility consultant: We've got an incomplete picture here. Partly what's missing is the industrialised world's role in the post colonial failures which we need to remember as we deal with the sensitive debates of today, otherwise we could be a bit complacent. Partly what's missing is the excessive focus on simple financial indicators of well-being – Amartya Sen is one of the many independent economists who would doubt that the world's majority are better off today. And the idea of NGOs terrorising meek governments and business into wearing sandals and eating lentils isn't something I see – we have an incomplete picture but all of it is part of the whole. What encourages me is that some leading corporations are getting to a more rounded picture – taking on board social responsibility, forming new partnerships, but they're a very small minority and this is fifteen years after Brundtland, so I'm wondering what bit of the message isn't getting through – what are we saying today which is different from fifteen years ago, and if we're here in fifteen years time what will we be saying which is different from today?

Chris Patten: First both as a minister and as a commissioner I have tried to develop at every level, both using them for development work in the field and using them as part of the policy-creation process. I've been very keen on developing my relationship with NGOs but not all NGOs are saints and not all multinational corporations are sinners. What is interesting today is very often how much better resourced NGOs are than public sector, either national or international, organisations. I was in Geneva for meetings with the human rights agency there. It is almost certainly the case that Amnesty International, which I greatly admire, is better resourced than the UN human rights agencies. And you could think of examples in one sector after another. So a gallant little NGO isn't always quite how it seems when you're in an international organisation. And it's not how it'll seem to the president of the World Bank when he has to confront 10,000 lobbyists from NGOs in Washington this spring, the consequence of whose actions would probably be that he had less money to spend in the developing world, helping developing countries to develop. Secondly, the point about the gap between rich and poor. I strongly believe that it is offensive that there are still so many people living in appalling poverty in parts of the world when we spend as much as we do in Europe on ice cream or pet food or whatever. And the UN development programme has produced many examples of that obscenity. But most objective looks at the figures suggest that probably the only two decades since the end of the Industrial Revolution when there hasn't been an opening gap between the rich and the poor has been the 1980s and the 1990s.

Ralph Sheppard, Ireland: Can sustainability be made to work in the real world? Self-seeking political parties are to blame for never taking the long view. They have to take the lead in making life-style changes feasible and attractive and making business and institutional changes inescapable.

Julian Filokowski from the aid agency, Cafod:
One of the big questions at the heart of the subject
remains unanswered. Nation states are smart enough to
recognise that sovereignty has to be pooled in some
areas but they're incapable of generating the public loyalty to those institutions that they create, and that into
the gap floods the tide of NGOs and pressure groups.
NGOs and pressure groups cannot make up for the
democratic deficit in those world organisations –
they're no substitute for democracy. The question,
then, is how can governments together with NGOs and
the rest of civil society create world institutions that will
be seen as legitimate and that can really effectively tackle
problems that flow across frontiers, like global warming,
drug trafficking, financial speculation – and organisations strong enough truly to regulate bodies like
transnational corporations?

Chris Patten: People feel their primary loyalty in a
political sense to the institutions of a nation state. When
that nation state hands over real authority in order to
protect its national interests to an international organisation, the loyalties don't travel with it. People may ratio-
nally comprehend that it's in their interests that this
should be done, but nobody feels a whoosh of pleasure
when the acronym IMF or the words World Bank are
mentioned – nobody has yet climbed a mountain and
put the European Union's flag at the top – though I

hope it will come to that. So it's a real problem. It is unwise if we try to approach it, to be candid, just by opening the relationship to NGOs, though that's something we have to do as well. We also have to look at parliamentary institutions. It's not a direct or strictly direct parallel but it's interesting that there has never been any serious questioning of NATO and the pooling of sovereignty in NATO, and NATO has always enjoyed the benefits of a parliamentary assembly and a real feeling of involvement by national parliamentarians in its governance, so we need to look at models like that.

Rowan Salim, from Holland Park School: You mentioned how non government organisations should be more interactive with governments. Doesn't this contradict their purpose, given that they benefit from their independence?

Chris Patten: An interesting thing about many non governmental organisations today is that they're almost entirely dependent on government or the public purse for their resources. And that raises interesting questions for them. It also has to be said that in an ideal world for NGOs they would rise and decline rather than always assert their right to be there. There's no reason why just because an NGO has done a good job on one particular issue it should be sustained for ever by government largesse or by demands on private charity. So I accept that the non government bit in the title is important. It is not always sufficiently recognised by NGOs today. It does not compromise NGOs to be involved in the making of policy with government, and it does not compromise government either.

In the 1970s the French population began to decline. The French government were worried about the future effect this would have on the economy of the country, as fewer people meant less money from taxes. They therefore introduced a tax system that encouraged the re-growth of the population, so twenty years down the line they would be able to free up more money for the government.

Is that a sustainable government policy and why couldn't this system be reversed? There you go, a method that doesn't directly harm anyone physically. It might mean hardship but I think that's a small price to pay.

John Barnes, UK

Many of the themes are addressed within the UK Governmental Department for International Development's White Paper of 1997. In particular I would like to draw attention to an approach that aims to reduce poverty by sustaining peoples' livelihoods, drawing on their strengths, rather than focusing on people's weaknesses.

This is known as the Sustainable Livelihoods Approach. It draws on international development success over the last twenty years and attempts to learn from mistakes. It is focusing on sustainability of livelihoods from an institutional, ecological and economic angle. Many of the principles of the SLA were referred to in the Reith lectures such as:

- the need to be holistic in our thinking, identifying the most pressing constraints faced by people
- the need to put people and their priorities at the heart of development and to respect their views
- stress the need to influence policies and international agreements and processes to be pro people, especially poor people
- to be dynamic and understand change by identifying supportive patterns and mitigating negative patterns
- build on strengths and recognise peoples' inherent strengths (human, social, natural, physical, financial)
- the recognition of how policies, laws and structures need to reflect the needs, and be informed by, local level lessons and insights.

There is a DFID website dedicated to supporting knowledge and learning about Sustainable Livelihood Approaches (to be found at www.livelihoods.org) which contains valuable guidance notes, a range of tools, case study material and an opportunity for people to share experiences.

Dr Jane Clark, UK

Sustainable development is not so much a matter of good governance as of our concept or model of development. Mahatma Gandhi said in 1927 that nature can give human beings enough to meet their needs but not to fulfil their greed. Unfortunately, humanity has forgotten his message. Developing countries have followed the Western model of pursuit of insatiable materialism. The developed countries would have to give a lead by conscious step to curb rampant materialism reflected in their style of living. They need governments which can follow such policies which may be unpopular.

Dr P.R. Dubhashi, India

Tom Lovejoy – Questions and Answers

Gordon Labaedz – leader of the southern Californian Sierra Club: The Sierra Club is the largest volunteer activist environmental organisation in the United States, and what we've found is that sustainable development has become a buzz word for human-centred destruction of the wild planet, and if in fact sustainable development is something that's enacted for humans, it is to diminish air pollution and to have good drinking water, etc. – I would question whether or not it maybe more reasonable, at least from an environmental activist point of view, to look at it from the animals' and the plants' point of view rather than just the humans' point of view.

Thomas Lovejoy: That is precisely why I have come to the conclusion that you really need to have a biological measure as to whether a piece of landscape is being treated in a sustainable fashion, because otherwise there's no real way to know whether you've actually passed certain limits or not, so in many senses, I subscribe entirely to your point of view.

Cathleen Cox – director of research at the Los Angeles Zoo: I am species co-ordinator for the Drill, which is one of the most endangered primates on the continent of Africa. My observation has been that when people are told they can't continue to pursue their livelihood there's a lot of resistance, for example in the centre of California the Tiger Salamander has just been declared endangered and the farmers there are being told they can't till the same soil as they did before – in Nigeria the Drill is so endangered that the local villagers are being told they can't hunt bush meat. And individuals don't want to give up immediate rewards in trade for some of the potential problems in the future being alleviated and in fact in the future they may not be around – they know they have to bear the cost of the problem, so my question really is – how can we make the future more important to today's population?

Tom Lovejoy: That question goes to the basic heart of everything about environment and a number of other issues as well – the short-term versus the long-term. And I think it is easier to do it if you have a larger framework, so if you're looking at a situation in a larger piece of landscape which can provide other opportunities which are not destructive of the biology, then it is easier to come to some kind of resolution. In a sense, you are telling somebody they can't do something but you're also giving them something else they can do. And all of that is fine and dandy but in the end it also comes down to the total number of people in a piece of landscape and you know what the impact is per individual – and that varies greatly around the world, from huge impact of North Americans as opposed to some people from the Third World, so it is a major challenge, no question about it.

Jo Turner, UK: The problem we face is not that there is too little food or too few resources but that we in the West use more than our fair share.

Bill White, executive director of the Orang-utan Foundation International: You set a couple of alarms that I'm not sure everyone's quite hearing – one is the global warming effect and the other is losing our rain forests. We have to find a way to have the World Bank work together with the IMF to work with other countries, to work with corporations and to work at the local level, giving these people jobs – or else you know as well as I do that they're going to take chain saws and cut down the trees.

Tom Lovejoy: You would be astonished at how hard the President of the World Bank had to work to get the World Bank board to accept this small conservation grant programme – I mean it has taken four years. And he finally gave them each a big book on hot spots and said 'you don't get it – go home and read this all night'. Just to underscore the climate change issue – all the glaciers on top of high mountains in the tropics are melting at a rate that they're going to be gone in twenty years and our nuclear submarine data on the thickness of the arctic ice sheet is now analysed and it lost 40 per cent since the initial period of measurement and it is on the average only six feet thick and it is losing four inches a year so you can do the arithmetic – that's less than twenty years. And that begins to tie into the whole global oceanic climate influence, so it's quite spooky.

Jeff Lin, school student, San Marino High: What do you see as the role of biotechnology such as genetic engineering in biodiversity?

Tom Lovejoy: Genetically modified organisms as a technology is like any technology, it has pluses and it has minuses – it can be used for good and it can be used for ill. It's come on very fast, driven by competition in big corporations. It came on too fast. On the other hand, if it becomes the way to produce rice enriched with vitamin A, so that a billion people in the world don't have the threat of blindness early in their life, that is a positive. At the same time you have to be very careful about the potential environmental effects. Regulation and labelling is a sensible way to go. But in the end, there will be biotechnology – the question is how thoughtfully and carefully will we manage it. My biggest fear about biotechnology is that it will create agricultural plants which can grow in places where they didn't grow before, so there will be more pressure on the remaining natural habitats of the world.

Daniel Emmett – actor and conservationist: Biodiversity clearly has to be the measure of how we're doing. When our daisies start disappearing and our birds that's a problem. What is being done in terms of cataloguing what's out there? We don't even know quite what is in our forests and in our rivers and in our oceans, and if this is going to the measure, as it should be, what's going on to really find out what we've got so we can use that to change policies and our behaviour?

Tom Lovejoy: It is nothing short of scandalous that we probably only know one out of every ten species on earth, let alone where they are or, various aspects of their biology, and I for one continue to try to launch a new age of exploration in which we explore the biology of our earth, a lot of which would blow people's minds. I keep trying to push that in Washington and periodically I get closer to it and then it ebbs away, but I think you're quite right. Unless we really know what there is, and where it is, we're going to make some mistakes without even knowing we've made them.

Bob Gillespie – President of Population Communication: The population of the planet has doubled in the last thirty-eight years and will double again in the next fifty to sixty years from 6 to 12 billion. Given that and the fact that the United States, with 4.8 per cent of that population, produces 26 per cent of our greenhouse gases? What hope is there for protecting the environment when everybody on the planet wants to live like we do?

Tom Lovejoy: I'm really glad you brought up both the population and the consumption issues together. There are now too many people on earth for everybody to live an American lifestyle. And there are also too many people on earth for everybody to live something closer to a hunter–gatherer lifestyle, so the answer lies somewhere in between and it's really complicated and it's going to be a transformation in the history of human society.

Perhaps the only way to bring about the fundamental change needed in our way of life is to teach the young. Habits are difficult to change once they are set. In my experience, as a restaurant owner employing a few teenagers for part-time work, young people don't have a clue about the environment. For example, we recycle wherever possible, including plastic bags from the supermarket, yet each time our young staff shop they return with yet more plastic bags rather than take with them a used bag from the last visit. A small point when we are trying to save the earth but the point is they have never been told, as far as I can make out, at school, why it is important not to squander natural resources. In fact one girl asked me what plastic is made of when I tried to explain that the stuff hangs around 'forever' and doesn't rot. Should not the basics of looking after the environment be taught in school from a young age? So much easier to take these things on board from the start. A sense of awe and wonder was mentioned, perhaps science should be taught at school not as a career choice but in the same way as art and literature, for the sheer joy of knowing how wonderful is this precious world in which we all live. I feel the more one learns about nature, and to me science is about understanding nature, the more you have to respect it. Without even referring to a 'Creator' it is awe inspiring in its intelligence.

Lesley Alkin, UK

I believe that recent science of complex systems concerns the fact (scientific) that systems are not mechanical. In order to represent some piece of reality as a mechanical system, at least four assumptions must be made. First, that a boundary can be drawn around the system, distinguishing it from the 'environment', that we know which are the explanatory components and features to be explained, and that our system has stereotypic components engaged in processes with 'average' rates. If these hold, then we may indeed claim to be able to predict behaviour and to have the system 'under control'. We may even optimise its constituents and mechanisms according to our goals. However, these assumptions, the basis of Newtonian mechanics, are not true in general. The microdiversity and local experiences that characterise reality mean that systems are therefore the seat of learning and co-evolutionary processes which necessarily have unknown consequences. Because of this, we therefore know that!

Rationality cannot be a sufficient basis for action! Any 'proven' model of a phenomenon must be calibrated and validated only on the past, and for the factors that we have thought of studying. In reality any design, investment, action or decision will really provoke consequences and responses which can only be guaranteed in the confines of a 'closed', laboratory system. Not the real world. For a theoretical physicist like myself this is a real shock. But most scientists have not yet understood the point, and continue to view the world as if it were a Newtonian machine, with predictable behaviour and hence open to manipulation. However, this belief itself is clearly misguided since the predictability of any system would be compromised by any manipulation other than by 'us'.

The understanding that is arising from complex systems thinking provides a theoretical basis for a 'precautionary attitude' if not principle, since we must also explore. It also provides a basis for microdiversity as being the source of resilience and of creativity in things. For many years I have worked on attempting to develop integrated frameworks to provide information about the possible consequences of investments, changes, actions envisaged. These link the soils, vegetation, crop choices, geomorphology, hydrology, water abstraction, waste production, urban and rural systems all in an interacting dynamic spatial representation. These have been supported mainly by the European Commission. However, I am now the Director of an ESRC Priority Network on the sustainability of socio-economic systems.

I believe that our work provides a solid conceptual framework for articulating the doubts that the Prince of Wales and some of the other speakers expressed. This framework comes from a scientific approach that demonstrates the limits of scientific rationality. If some see scientific rationality as the crowning glory of human achievement, then what can we say of the achievement that uses that framework to demonstrate its own inadequacy?

I do believe therefore that it is important to separate 'science' and an honest, systematic exploration of nature that scientists might make, with the commercial exploitation of that partial understanding, which tends to make unstated, but profitable, assumptions about what is 'safe' and 'certain' – until it isn't of course.

I believe that the complex systems framework that has been developed over the last decade can provide a means of communication between different 'stakeholders' in society. It can make clear the assumptions, values and motivations of the different players in the system, and force an open discussion and analysis of what is known, what is not really known, and why something should or should not be done.

Professor Peter M. Allen, Cranfield School of Management, Cranfield University, UK

Although I am worried about GM foods and their effect on the environment, I feel that much more research must be done to make the public feel that the technique is safe. What most people do not realise is that we are already eating a form of GM foods as many of the goods in the food chain are the result of selective growing techniques, i.e. cross pollination, grafting and weeding out of less healthy looking plants and animal species.

GM is just a much faster way of providing this, and once it is found to be safe, will help reduce famine.

Eileen Henshaw, England

I arrived two and a half years ago in New Zealand hoping to find a cleaner greener future for my daughter. I was sadly mistaken. Chemicals such as 1080 are top-dressed indiscriminately over huge areas to kill possums, and now they are discussing using GE (genetically engineered) carrots despite a thriving new industry for possum fur and merino blend yarns. On reaching Nelson I joined a local anti-GE group in 1998 proceeding to canvass public opinion and make submissions against GE crop applications through the Environmental Risk Management Authority. All GE trials have been approved to date by this quasi-judiciary body which has no automatic independent research funding or external independent assessment but must bid to get funding to prepare reports on risks, their first (on antibiotic resistant marker genes) due to be released in June, two years after their first GE approval.

The majority of GE research is now carried out in Crown Research Institutes partially funded by the Public Good Science Fund and partially from other sometimes more dubious sources. PPL have permission to run a GE trial application in containment of 10,000 GE sheep with human genes. A recent application for cows with human genes has been stalled by Maori protest, the Maori genealogy and culture forbidding the mixing of genes.

Yes, we are due to have a Royal Commission of Inquiry starting soon and have a voluntary moratorium on crops in place during the proceedings but nothing has really changed. Major multinationals buy into New Zealand because 'the land is cheap and the regulations relatively lax' (*Sunday Times* 9.1.2000). It is not right that the people are ignored when they wish only to have choice and protect their environment from the unproven benefits and many dangers of genetic pollution that genetic engineering holds.

Susie Lees, New Zealand

It is vain in the extreme to assume that, because we cannot foresee any damaging consequences to health and the environment from the release of GM organisms, there will be no damaging consequences. It was this assumption which led to the BSE crisis after all. It is also vain to assume that we can control the effects, known and unknown, of this technology on health, wealth and the ecosystem. Let's proceed, but with extreme caution, tight controls and a safety-assured backout plan.

Francis O'Leary, UK

Too many words. What we want is action. No GE for example. No one seems to explain exactly how dangerous it is. People say genetic modification has been carried out for centuries, and they are right. But, and it cannot be emphasised more, the modern 'genetic engineering' is not the same thing at all. We are breaking down natural barriers, increasing disease etc., etc. Find out all about it, of course. Knowledge is power.

We have to reconcile that we cannot control this planet, and we have to find ways to live within it, be happy in this and not continually strive to be always bigger, better, richer, more powerful, etc., etc.

You have all heard the arguments too many times before, and yet still the wisdom does not shine through. I'm not a religious person at all, just an honest one. One that hopes she is not too close to despair, but in the morning I get up again and work at getting my seven acres of organic orchard to the paradise that the whole world could also be if we truly wanted.

Celia Wilson, New Zealand

John Browne – Questions and Answers

Sarah Boyack, Scottish Minister for Transport and the Environment: Ninety-three per cent of our businesses in Scotland are small- or medium-sized enterprises. How do we work with them to begin to get them to see the self-enlightenment, the collective enlightenment, to look to the future for sustainable development – on issues like waste or energy or travel – where it is more difficult to think of the long-term because there are short-term economic pressures. How do we work with those types of organisations to bring about the change and the connectedness that you discussed?

John Browne: The key is the incentive. How do you get people to start thinking in this way? This is the vital and real role for government, to start the process off, not necessarily to finish the process, but to start it off, giving people a way of feeling proud about what they're doing, giving them some financial help, and the knowledge to do what is necessary to do the business better.

Jeremy Peat, Chief Economist at the Royal Bank of Scotland: I'm less optimistic than you are that pure enlightenment is the way forward. I suggest that there maybe some necessity to introduce some form of market based instrument that provides the correct signals for companies large and small in this area. I would emphasise the importance of efficiency and competitiveness in the world going forward, and I believe that the market does work efficiently, but it needs the right signals as well as the enlightenment.

John Browne: *In extremis* you are right – clearly there has to be a level playing field and those who are prepared to opt out of explaining what they're doing with transparency, feeling accountable for what they have done, setting targets, coming back and showing how the targets have been fulfilled, then there needs to be something which constrains those who are not prepared to play that game, for they will in the end be free-loaders on a society that's trying to do something different.

Bill Speirs, General Secretary, Scottish Trade Union Congress: On the role of democratic governments in a world of globalisation, we've had a very interesting decision by the United States judiciary, that they are prepared to intervene in the operation and the structure of the biggest, most powerful company in the world, Microsoft. Would you see that as a positive or a negative development?

John Browne: There is a clear role for governments to look at the nature of competition, and to make sure that competitive forces are alive and well – that companies don't, simply by their sheer scale, chill the nature of innovation. Governments need to ensure that companies do actually conduct themselves in a way that is level and appropriate for all the customers, and encourage people to compete with them so that better and better things can be produced. That has been a fundamental basis for so much of competition regulation in the world. The consequences in specific cases have to be looked at on their individual merits.

Prof. Gareth Owen, Heriot-Watt University: What is the role of renewable technologies and also the relationship between your companies and the development of renewable technologies and the impact that can make in the future?

John Browne: It's an interesting misnomer that in every introduction we are called an oil company. We're not an oil company, we're a gas company with oil, with lots of other associated energies. Renewable energy is one of those things. Technology is very much improving and we are improving the photo-voltaic section of renewable energies – so-called solar energy. It is a great form of energy because photons from the sun are abundantly available. The key is how to make them convert into electricity efficiently and practically. We have a business that's growing at about 20 per cent a year in this area. It takes a long time however for any of this to have a very big impact on the world because it starts from small roots. The roots are small enough to say if you added up all the solar energy in the world and added it up for a year, it would power Germany for three days. Now that's better than one and it will get bigger at 20 per cent growth rate, as time goes by. But not immediately. This is all to do with transitions in the mix of fuels.

Dr Camilla Toulmin, International Institute for Environment and Development, Edinburgh: We seem to be living in a set of parallel worlds which were so clearly exemplified by the riots in Seattle at the end of last year, and also in the anti GM crop movements which demonstrate a very deep level of concern felt by many people about the consequences of continued economic growth and globalisation and the absence of public trust. How does an organisation like BP try to engage with such debates and position itself in this changing field of public opinion?

John Browne: The first level answer is that we do actually engage. It's very important that we talk to people not like ourselves. We need to talk to people with a wide variety of opinions and seek out what is actually the issue at hand and whether the issue can allow for a solution. It may be that opinions are so polarised that it is impossible to reach a point of some understanding, but these situations are rare. There is a clear role for business in bringing together technology, experience and world-wide understanding and saying that what business offers is progressive. We ask government to make decisions on behalf of democracies of selections of people who they represent. We then ask those who wish to test both to come and see how the two things can be put together. That's the best we can do, and it does work, not always however.

Fred Grunier, Tasmania: Governments should use interest rates to encourage ethical investment. There should be a penalty on loans used for land speculation and lower interest rates for small businesses which are ecologically sound.

Andrew Ketley, UK: What Sir John completely fails to mention is that while companies may be interested in their long-term economic survival, their shareholders and creditors in the main are not. For the banks and the big institutional investors what matters is short-term profit.

John Browne: It's very kind to make a fault line but I do not think the fault line exists. Shareholders in the end invest in the long-term, not necessarily the same people the whole time, but there are shareholders that do that. What they want to see, as banks do, is good plans. They want to see people lay out what they want to do over a run of years and then come back and tell them how they're doing from time to time. That is how you keep shareholders and banks with you. If you give them a plan, give them targets and you give them a report back then they are into this for the long-term. Certainly for my company, it takes ages for us to do lots of things, like develop oil fields in the North Sea. It took almost ten years. Even with the best technology, now maybe we could cut it by 50 per cent. Five years is a long time. That's the sort of patience that banks and shareholders need to and do have.

Christopher Cairns, Environment Correspondent at the *Scotsman*: You mentioned that new technology will be able to deliver sustainable development – that is presumably partly the justification for exploring for more oil and gas – for example the Atlantic margin. Is it justifiable for you to rely on as yet unproven technologies to deliver sustainable development when the precautionary approach, relying more on renewables, would seem more sensible?

John Browne: It is an interesting concept of whether we can only rely on today's technology to do anything in the future. I totally disagree with that and had anyone done that we would not have had the Internet. We certainly wouldn't have micro-processors at the speed presently available. Nor actually would we have had the development of the North Sea gas industry or oil industry. At the time the first steps were taken no one had an idea of how to actually use the technology in a way which made sense. It's only taking those steps and learning from those steps, building with the idea that you can always do something better, does the technology arrive. Simply to rely on today's technology for the future and not to allow a variety of technologies to blossom and bloom, such as cleaner fuels, emissions-free electricity generation – which may lead to sustainability – to deny all that would set back enormously the progress of the world and the world economy.

Christopher Cairns: You have said in the past that you think new technology will allow us to be able to burn all the oil and gas that we need to meet world demand and not ruin the environment – so these new technologies that you seem to be investing in are technologies to allow you to continue to use old fuel rather than investing in what some people would say are the real technologies of tomorrow, which are the renewables?

John Browne: This is like saying the only use of copper is to take electricity and take it from *a* to *b*. That's not true. There are lots of other things that copper is used for – or take silicon, which is sand. Sand is used for building, that's certainly true, but it's also the substrate for the most powerful micro-processors in the world. You have to think of different uses and adapt and adopt products as we go forward. The argument about whether more exploration should be permitted is complex. But to explore for oil is to have the option to develop it. We have no idea how much oil we will need. We don't know how much oil will be developed over time. But to deny the choices to the world in advance of having a clear cut solution to substitute is premature in the extreme, especially as the technologies allow us to make very different things that we haven't thought of in the past. The gallon of petrol that you buy today bears no relationship to the gallon that you bought ten or even twenty years ago. It's a very different substance and I can't believe it won't stop changing. It'll change as will the engines that burn it.

Lorraine Mann: I live in the Highlands of Scotland where I do some campaigning against nuclear dumping and I represent a number of renewable energy companies professionally. When exactly do we get to the point of acknowledging that an entire technological route that we have been pursuing was in fact, with the benefit of hindsight, a mistake, and when we do discover that what should we do about it?

John Browne: There are always quite big, strategic mistakes made by the world. A long time ago in the 70s, we concluded that there was such an abundance of crude oil that the best way to deal with it would be to make it into animal feed. We invented the most brilliant technological process so to do. And fortunately the price of oil went up so the technology couldn't work. So it was abandoned and a good thing too. The recognition of the mistake normally is on the basis, at least in business, of two things. One is the economics in the end don't work, so it becomes very expensive to do something. And second, the sheer pressure from the shareholders, governments, the staff, the employees and society generally too. And then things get changed. In our company's case there are half a dozen stories I can tell you like that.

Hugh Raven: I live in North Argyle, on the west coast of Scotland, where we've recently seen increasing evidence of climate change. Could you use your influence as a leader of the oil industry to try to persuade your peers, in the United States in particular, to take more seriously the threat of climate change and perhaps begin to take seriously their responsibilities after the Kyoto agreement?

John Browne: We have had a lot of discussion with the rest of the oil industry. We believed as a company that precautionary action had to be taken to mitigate the emissions of CO_2 and greenhouse gases into the atmosphere. When we took this position we were not the most popular oil company in the club of oil companies. However, a lot of discussion is now going on. And the good news is that a lot of companies work in partnership, which means that the influence of thinking, technology and approach begins to spread. Compared with three years ago the oil industry is in much better shape, but there is much more to do. It will take time to persuade everyone that the right course of action is to take some precautions.

Dr Brian Fenton, Scottish Crop Research Institute: You talked about the importance of transparency to business. Do you think that governments are sufficiently transparent?

John Browne: When you ask a businessman this question the answer is usually no. In any big system, like governments, there can always be more transparency. But the transparency everyone really wants is the bits that governments are less likely to give, such as; where really is the money going; what's really happening to the things that everybody wants to know about but can't actually see because they're secret? Those sorts of things. Business has not been very transparent until relatively recently. A lot of mistakes in business have led to a lot of policies being put in place and, of course, the whole change of the way in which information spreads around the world in an extraordinary way has encouraged people to be more and more transparent. It is probably going to happen to government too as time goes by.

Linda Fabiani, Member of the Scottish Parliament: Respect for the earth also means respect for the earth's people and unfortunately some multinational companies have very poor reputations in regard to the indigenous peoples in poorer countries amongst which they work. How important to multinational companies do you think human rights are?

John Browne: Our role is to engage wherever we can and to demonstrate that we're actually doing something that makes a positive difference, however small. BP stayed in South Africa during a very tough time during apartheid bringing our own employees to a different level of educational qualification, maximising the number of black people working inside our company. This was not wholly popular at the time but it sowed small seeds which subsequently grew to enormous trees; some great people were available to populate part of the government, great people were there to populate part of industry. The same is true in more modern experiences. Engagement does help people in Colombia for example, and in Russia or the republics of Russia where education programmes can help build a different way of life and a different way of thinking. The specifics are all different depending on where you are. The test is: when you're gone, have you left something behind? And have you actually invested in the society of which you want to be part of?

Christine Marshall, Postgraduate student in Environment and Development at the University of East Anglia: I would like to think business, in the shape of oil companies, has changed its spots. However, hearing the personal testimonies against Shell and Chevron, of the Ogoni peoples from the Niger Delta of persecution, intimidation, bribery, murder, environmental destruction and extreme poverty, he will per-haps forgive me for knowing otherwise. So-called 'green' initiatives by Shell in Norway and UK deceive those in the West about the real nature and intention of industry to get away with whatever it can in developing countries, at whatever cost to the poorest. Will they rise to the challenge of transparency, public pressure and morality here?

All of the lecturers seem to agree that there is a problem, but none of them get to the nub of it. Basically there are two interrelated problems – economic growth and pop-ulation growth. Neither of these can be sustained indef-initely. What economic growth really means is consumption growth, and the present economic sys-tems depend upon it; we must grow more food, build on more land, chop down more trees, catch more fish, destroy more wildlife habitat etc. etc., year on year or else we have unemployment, stagnation, recession etc. etc. Population growth simply compounds the prob-lem, because year on year there are more people, each of whom has to consume more. In a world of finite resources, per capita consumption can only increase if population declines. Proposed solutions to population growth such as 'eliminating poverty' must be viewed in this light. Eliminating poverty simply means poor people consuming more, and this can only occur if rich people consume less, unless overall consumption of world resources increases, which is what we should be trying to prevent. That is the enormity of the problem. Nothing less than a new theory of economics is required, which does not depend upon ever-increasing consumption. 'Globalisation' will only make things worse, i.e. lead to more consumption. There is no 'sustainable' development.

L. Andrews, UK

The divide which has occurred between man and nature has driven humanity into a state of greed, control and a need for personal wealth and power. All out ideals have been transformed from what we need to obtaining our desires – at any cost. We have lost the fundamental principles of life. Globalisation is a force that has been pushed by the wealthiest 5 per cent of the world's population. It is this proportion of people that actually benefit, 95 per cent of the world's peoples, as well as the earth in which we all evolved with and other creatures have been left with little consideration.

How can we stop this? How can we turn around the dominant western ideals? If we don't we will be destroyed. People will starve and the standard of living can only dissipate whilst the top 5 per cent continue to fill their already overflowing bank accounts.

At birth everyone is blessed with the ability of becoming anything. Why do we teach our children to walk the road of destruction rather than a road of life, respect and love? It makes me ashamed to be a part of the human family. I can only think of one other animal in which we come close – the rat. However, that potential at birth is always with us – this is our hope, is it too late?

Denise La Grouw, New Zealand

The crucial problem with these lectures – as more generally – is that the political/business establishment completely fails to recognise the seriousness of the sustainability crisis. One figure which demonstrates this is that we need to reduce our fossil fuel consumption to only 40 per cent of its present level to – eventually – halt global warming. Yet the establishment has no aim or intention of achieving this figure. What can be done about the complacency of the political/business establishment?

Tony Hamilton, Pool Agenda 21, UK

If we're really serious about joined-up thinking and dealing with CO_2 problems, shouldn't we be thinking about industries that produce CO_2 being required to subsidise, for example, the kind of small farmer that keeps twelve month grass cover on the land they use, keeps the maximum number of hedges growing, keeps small patches of woodland or scrub and so on? Precisely not the large agri-business farms that get the vast majority of subsidies at the moment? Isn't this a better reason to subsidise farmers than 'preserving the historic land-scape', which is largely artificial anyway?

Jacky Smith, Britain

Gro Harlem Brundtland – Questions and Answers

Dr Tesfamichael Ghebrehewet, Nurse Consultant with International Council of Nurses: To quote an African saying – 'the best time to plant your tree is 20 years ago – the next best time is now.' Now is the time to reflect on the old and to plant the trees for a healthy future. How can the health sector, and health profession-als in particular, be effectively aligned with other sectors to better address the health needs of the population?

Gro Harlem Brundtland: Clearly the health profes-sionals, widely defined, are absolutely essential to be able to both mobilise the awareness and to deliver what is needed. However, it sometimes happens that health professionals struggle very hard to get sufficient aware-ness about the situation that they are faced with. And so to increase and widen the awareness into much broader parts of our societies and to get the attention of the finance minister and the prime minister is essential. But without the health professionals and without everybody in the NGO or other parts who support our work, we would never be able to reach our goals.

Annar Cassam, UNESCO director, Geneva: Mozambique. Before the floods, before the skies opened up over Mozambique recently, Mozambique was spending 3 per cent of its resources on education and health, and 33 per cent on debt service. The Paris Club have refused to cancel Mozambique's debt but have deferred it. You talked about resources and the need for resources in Mozambique is obviously huge, but you also mentioned the words, 'loan sharks'. I'd be interested to know how this category of loan shark country can be asked to engage in this particular debate, because obviously the arguments based on moral persuasion or on enlightened self-interest wouldn't work. What would work?

Gro Harlem Brundtland: In January 2000, some of us were assembled in Davos at the World Economic Forum to launch the GAVI – the Global Alliance for Vaccines and Immunisations. One of the people on the panel with me was the President of Mozambique. It was before the flood, but he had been asked to participate as a representative of the least developed countries who are really the ones which we need to support and help to get vaccines, which is the shared goal of the initiators of the GAVI initiative.

As we were talking, the President of Mozambique, in addition to addressing health and immunisation, made the point about the general great problems that his country was facing. He mentioned the debt problem. He mentioned the infrastructure challenges. And none of us at that moment had any idea of what was going to unfold in the coming weeks. We certainly need to find solutions which both take care of the debt problems but also see to it that what is being invested in are the things that are most essential for the people, whether in Mozambique or other debt-ridden countries of the least developed countries. The problems for governments who are donors and who try to support development are that one would like to support at least a development which would address some of the basic needs like education and health. Again it is increased awareness and continued focus on how these things are linked together. That opportunities, abilities, capacity building and the focus on the coming generation – which is what Mozambique's problem is about, along with so many other countries who need this support to move out of poverty and destitution.

Penny Grewel, Novatis Foundation for Sustainable Development: I work with WHO in Brazil and in Madagascar to eliminate leprosy and I have witnessed the tremendous potential of your organisation and the leverage that you have used in order to bring together diverse groups of people, get them to buy into unorthodox solutions. Do you think that more could be done in this respect?

Gro Harlem Brundtland: What we have achieved – the funding, the involvement of many NGO groups and others – is to fight a disease which carries a stigma, a disease which is now treatable with simple means as long as the medication is available and you reach the people who need it. I am optimistic about being able to tackle the question of leprosy.

D. Chambers, UK: If human population was diminishing instead of expanding, we would not be having this debate at all. The real debate should be about controlling the rampant growth of our species.

Gro Harlem Brundtland: A diminished population in itself would lead to other kinds of equity balances, focus on human rights, focus on the empowerment of women, the opportunities of children? It is not as simple as that. We have seen in the last thirty years that if they have opportunities, people choose to have fewer children. It is having knowledge, having opportunity, having the feeling that you have a future and that your children will live to be grown ups. Those kinds of situations are what make the changes. And we see that it works. I don't know of any way, any method of so-called controlling the number of people except in the indirect way of giving people choices, opportunities, access, and a decent dignity in life, so that family choices and people's own choices can be at the centre of the answer.

Kathleen Cravero, Deputy Director, United Nations programme on HIV Aids: Today nearly thirty-four million people are infected with HIV. Aids has become a full-blown development crisis and is on its way to becoming the single greatest threat to human security in Africa. Good health is a prerequisite for development. HIV Aids affects people in their most productive years and is fast wiping out many of the development gains that have taken decades to achieve. What are the key lessons, learned from combating other infectious diseases, that can now strengthen our response to the AIDS epidemic, and what are the priority actions?

Gro Harlem Brundtland: It's a dramatic epidemic or pandemic. One fifth of the working force in several African countries may be lost by this major threat which started in the last century, and which we really have to face with open discussion and with solidarity initiatives, not just so that people in the rich countries can deal with it, relate to it and be able to prevent and treat. There is also the question of looking at the global threat as something that affects us and that we have responsibility for our fellow human beings in other countries.

The issue of education seems to have been largely ignored in these debates, and yet Agenda 21 in Rio in 1992 stated that 'education is critical for promoting sustainable development'. In the UK the new curriculum rationale does mention its importance and brings in a new emphasis on citizenship. Surely all educators in the broadest sense have a duty to instil in young people a reverence for the awe and wonder of nature, but also to teach them to think critically about issues such as consumerism and show them that they can play a part in making changes for the better of all?

Clive Belgeonne, UK

Vandana Shiva – Questions and Answers

Sujata Gupta, the Tata Energy Research Institute: I'd like to hear your views on sustainable use of scarce inputs like water for agriculture. What I gathered from your lecture was total condemnation of the market system.

Vandana Shiva: I love markets. I love my local market where local 'subgees' [vegetables] are sold, and one can chat with the women. The tragedy really is that the market is being turned into the only organising principle for life, and Wall Street is being turned into the only source of value, and it's the disappearance of other markets, other values that I am condemning. In terms of water, the solution to water conservation and scarce water management is not putting it in the hands of those who can afford to buy the last drop, but to put it in the hands of the community, to use it sustainably within the limits of renewal. The water must be returned to the communities and managed – it has to be taken beyond the marketplace.

Professor Marva, University of Delhi: Can there be sustainable development without sustainable population?

Vandana Shiva: Non-sustainable population growth is a symptom and product of non-sustainable development. It's not that population grows by itself as a separate phenomena. The Indian population was stable until the eighteenth century, however colonisation and dispossession of land started to make our population grow. Highest growth rates of population in England occurred after the enclosure of the common land. It is the loss of resources that generate livelihood and the replacement of resources by labour to be sold on markets in an uncertain daily-wage-market that triggers population growth. Population growth is a result of non-sustainable development.

Dr Sandhya Tiwari, Confederation of Indian Industry: Is it really the job of the farmer to preserve germ plasm and biodiversity, to grow plants that are less productive? Shouldn't this job be left to the specialists?

Vandana Shiva: I'm talking about leaving it to the specialist, which is the women farmers. So far, if we have biodiversity available to us it is because biodiversity experts, who happen to be women by gender, happen to be on small farms in poorer parts of the world, have continued to conserve biodiversity because it is more productive for them from their perspective. It might not be productive for a single monopoly trading house that wants to have every farmer grow corn in a region or every farmer grow cornola in a region, but it is highly productive and very efficient use of land, water – to feed the family, to have a little surplus to sell on the local market, to send your child to school and it is in fact that community which will save these resources for us. We cannot trust them in anyone else's hands.

Anthony Giddens: I congratulate you on your challenging presentation. I have to say, though, I don't agree with much of it. Isn't it a contradiction in terms to use the global media to put a case against globalisation?

Vandana Shiva: The BBC is not a product of the economic globalisation regime that the World Trade Organisation gave us or the new recent trade liberalisation has given us. It was created in 1922 and international integration, international communication is not what economic globalisation is about. Corporate concentration, corporate control is what recent economic globalisation is about and in fact the BBC is a counter-example to that.

Rovinder Raki, student: You seem to eulogise the fairness and efficiency of traditional agricultures, societies and production patterns. But the reality is that the farmers were exploited in these societies by money-lenders and feudal lords. With the market reaching these societies, that exploitative social system certainly declined. What restrains you from appreciating this sanitising effect of the market?

Vandana Shiva: The sanitising effect of the market does end up treating people like germs. Wipe them out. And it is that view of dispensability, the disappearances of the small that I was trying to draw attention to. There has always been exploitation, but no exploitation before this period of current, economic globalisation, ever organised itself in ways that it could totally dispense with the exploited. Even the slave system needed the slave. Even the worst of British rule which created the Bengal famine, and led the 'Faybehaga' movement to rise against the exploitation, it needed to keep the peasants alive. For the first time we have a system where no one needs the peasants, unless we realise as societies that we need them.

We have to pay attention to the ecological base of our survival and the needs of all. I am committed to feeling and believing that the smallest of species and the smallest of people have as much a right to live on this planet with dignity as the most powerful corporation and the most powerful individual.

Rukmini Paya Naiur, professor at the Indian Institute of Technology: Some would argue [my institute] is exclusively focused on what you call the dot.com route to success. Listening to your strong emphasis on biodiversity, it struck me that there was an unseen shadow-twin of biodiversity which is recyclability or reusability in our cultures. India is said to be a great recycling culture – we recycle everything – including souls. Do you think this shadow-twin recycling had something to contribute to the notion that the materials of the whole universe are in fact reusable and that we have something to offer the world in this sort of expertise?

Vandana Shiva: We have been a civilisation that lived on the basis of recycling and that's why when we today are burdened with plastic and plastic packaging, now required by law, people still treat that plastic bag as if is a little banana leaf that will disappear. And even the cows are in the habit of thinking plastic is like a banana leaf they can eat up. Some products don't disappear. Some products don't get recycled and that's part of the crisis for a culture which has had such sensitive ways of ensuring that our ecological footprint is very light on the planet. Last year a scientist from Canada sent me his data on ecological footprint and his data on resource use, and the ability of eco-systems to absorb outputs and waste was that there were only three countries with surpluses in resources – Canada, Sweden and at that time, India. That was India before the race to 'plasticise' itself, to globalise itself. We need to fit into those systems that have evolved so sophisticatedly, recycling organic matter to ensure we get out of the chemical treadmill because chemicals do not get recycled. They just bio-accumulate.

P.D. Kayra from Delhi: While I appreciate that bio-diveristy and like–systems do help with production, I am more concerned with the farmer who today is disenchanted and less and less motivated and becoming totally indifferent to his way of life and that maybe bio-diversity by itself will not be able to explain?

Vandana Shiva: In the areas where monocultures have taken over, where external inputs and chemicals are forcing farmers to spend the little bit of income they have to buy those useless and costly inputs – farmers are disenchanted because of negative economy and the fact that the entire set of technologies in industrial agriculture are careless technologies. They are technologies that substitute care with carelessness. You can just spray urea – you don't have to do composting. You don't have to weed at the right time – the few tiny weeds that might come up, spray the herbicide. That technology of carelessness eventually creates disenchanted people because they have no meaning, no role. In the areas where we work through our movement called 'Navdanya', for conserving biodiveristy we now have seed banks in seven states, eleven community seed banks have been started – every region where after a while the farmers have replaced external inputs with internal inputs to produce food organically, where they have managed to get rid of their debts – a threefold increase in incomes just by saving on expenditure – they are excited, they're enthused, they are absolutely on the verge of a whole new determination and I invite some of you to come and visit those regions.

Recently heard in a classroom students were developing a new policy on the environment. The term 'stewardship' was adopted by the group completely independently of the term's use in the Reith lectures by HRH Prince Charles, because of the respect growing for Aboriginal and Indigenous 'Land' consciousness. The people belong to the land and thus an Aboriginal stewardship is an ecologically sustainable management of the land that establishes a sacred trust. Custody and custodial terminology is being displaced by a return to physical contact made by the key stakeholders. Major stakeholders are the children and women of the land. The latter have, for the large part of history, been given, and worldwide continue to be given the lowest priority. To have, and to maintain 'contact' with the land, the water and the air is the right of every child. Australia is still a land ravaged by other cultures and with the introduction of Local Agenda 21 Strategy and the maintenance of classroom forums on new environmental policy it may still yet be saved for future generations to enjoy.

Robert Cordia, Australia

The debate has been about the provision of health and education and the eradication of poverty, sustainable development and debt forgiveness, genetic engineering (aren't we clever!) and population issues. But no one has dared to mention the greatest shame on the planet, the unmentionable, the 250 million children outside any kind of social framework, the millions upon millions of street children living like rats in sewers, railway lockers and underground tunnels without parental or state care, without love. Girls of thirteen with a second generation of babies. Children who sniff glue and use other drugs just to forget for a while their unwantedness, their despair. The large numbers that commit suicide before they are fifteen. This is not a tragedy that can be blamed on poverty alone, or on ill health, or lack of education. It has as much, if not more, to do with sexual abuse, mostly by the immediate family, by greed and exploitation in the drugs and sex industry, in armies, in factories and in the mines, children in slavery, the railway children.

This has to do with an inbred human cruelty, human deprivation, human greed, which, according to the well-know environmentalist/biologist Professor Dr Bellamy makes the human species the worst amongst the world's mammals in their treatment of their off-spring. Yes, the human condition is a contributory factor, of course, but the real underlying reason is the inexplicable flaw in the human character. It is that which we all – if not share – are responsible for. That responsibility is awesome, as much for the human being as an individual as it is for governments, and too much to cope with or to admit to for most.

Trudy Davies, Hon. Director, European Network for Street Children Worldwide, London/Brussels

Chris Patten did not mention that the EU Common Agricultural Policy has done more environmental harm than anything which could have been devised. The small farmer/land owner is invariably more friendly to the environment but is being literally thrown off the land by the CAP, which favours big agri-businesses which in general have done and are doing great harm to the environment, while producing surpluses which are often dumped on the Third World, which in turn puts their small farmers out of business.

I think most people are delighted that HRH the Prince of Wales has taken such a strong line against genetic engineering – just an extension of agri-business.

Philip Greig, England

I listened with disbelief to the lecture by Vandana Shiva. First, she refers often to the role of women farmers, and to how they are deserving of respect for their knowledge. Yet she gives them no credit for making their own informed decisions about how they want to run their lives and their farms. How quaint, that she enjoys going to her local markets, and meeting the growers. Yet she assumes for these farmers that they do not want to adopt new technologies, or make changes in the way farming is practised. She assumes that they are all content with their current lot in life, or wish a return to 'the good old days'. She must think that they are not rational beings, who make decisions which they believe to be in their own best interests. She accuses multinational corporations of forcing their inputs and branded consumer goods on Indian farmers and consumers. Does she not have faith in her own countrymen and women to think for themselves?

The companies she criticises are not coercing farmers or consumers into buying their products, and in fact can only make sales if the purchaser sees value in the offer. If there was not a vitamin A deficiency problem, there would be no demand for vitamin A enhanced rice. If western-based companies refused to sell their products in India, on the grounds that the population was too ignorant or weak-willed to make good purchasing judgements, what reaction would she have then? India is a democratic nation. It has a higher proportion of poor than rich citizens. What explanation does she have for the freely-elected government making decisions and entering into agreements that she feels are against the will of the people? Ms Shiva refers to 'the rules of globalisation' without stating what she thinks they are and who she thinks makes them and enforces them.

She demonises all corporations and their employees, and by extension their customers. This, and the statement that they are driven by fear of all things living and free, is patently ridiculous. Another glaring issue which she barely touches on is the population explosion, which is so obvious in the week in which the official population of India topped one billion. Statistics will show that richer nations have lower birth rates and lower rates of infant mortality; and the economies of the rich countries are not based on small, subsistence farms. Can she really not grasp that so many people have a far greater impact on the biodiversity of species than seed varieties? Ms Shiva is obviously a passionate advocate for her beliefs about what is right for India. Too bad that she has so little respect for the beliefs of her fellow citizens. She could do a lot more good if she put her energies towards such critical issues as population control, education and religious/ethnic intolerance. And, by the way, the study that indicated that GM corn was a threat to Monarch Butterflies has been discredited (see the University of Guelph in Canada.)

Karen Kelsey, UK

It is impossible for me to imagine what it is like to be a peasant woman, who is self-sufficient and able to grow not only enough food for her family but to choose what she grows for them. I have a garden full of wild flowers, some of which I know are sources of food, but the knowledge of what those plants are as nutrition is lost to me. The Internet may well be a tool for retrieving that knowledge.

There are many side issues present in this debate, but what seems most clear is that neither the capitalist nor communist overviews (both of which are, at best, only long-drawn-out unconscious efforts to overthrow feudal oppression of one kind or another) are sufficient to encompass a truly human approach to globalisation. The most arrogant notion, put to me recently by an American was that to be a peasant farmer is necessarily an impoverished state. This probably reflects the opinion of many more of us who are completely swamped by the politics and values of corporate ethics and the consumption of the unnecessary. Is this a lie that the West is teaching the world for its own benefit or does it hold a seed of some truth?

Even if there is a semblance of truth in that view, it should be the voice of the peasant farmers who are heard first in this debate, speaking for themselves, above that of government and corporations. But do they have a platform on which to stand in order to be heard. Will they be given that chance? Until we listen, we have no idea what they have to teach us, what we may relearn about our humanity and ourselves. But it is not surprising to hear such a view, when we consider that European colonisers were and still are members of a fully fledged political and agricultural power house, who were either escaping from its oppression or seeking to expand its power, who excused their own savage behaviour by describing the indigenous people whom they met as underdeveloped savages. Were they unable to conceive of the possibility that any human historical or evolutionary process, not entirely born out of the murderous excesses of ancient Greece or Rome, whose philosophies still seem to have a stranglehold on our lives, may be as important or valid as our own?

It seems that a global dialogue, which could include everyone is only just beginning. Can we be trusted to listen and not pillage; not to use the abstraction of capitalism as a disguised tool of oppression; not to prey upon the weakness inherent in all our natures; not to become more and more blind to the true nature of our own impoverishment?

Until we in the so-called civilised world are able fully

167

to understand our impoverishment; where the seat of that impoverishment lies; and what exactly we can do about it, we will simply continue blindly fulfilling the will of the dragon in its path of destruction. At present we have no mandate to dictate to the developing world other than to bow our heads in shame, for that which has been imposed on her life that she does not need, for her people who have been destroyed and all that has been plundered from her in the process.

Geraldine Perowne, England

Vandana Shiva was the only lecturer who lived up to the intellectual challenge, especially in her concerns for biodiversity in farming systems as run largely by peasants and mostly by women. Increasing voices such as these have consistently been ignored. I know that when I recently talked to the Zimbabwe Farmers Union leader he dismissed the bambarra nut (Vigna subterranea) as commercially unviable and yet this crop among many are perfect for the environment and for food security.

Sekani Tikondelwe, Wales

General Questions and Answers

Jonathon Porritt states that the Prince of Wales has been engaged in the debate on sustainable development for many years. Debate however normally manifests itself in contributors responding to challenges to their point of view. The BBC however allowed a contribution where no challenges were directly accepted. Is this commensurate with an open process?

The contribution of Prince Charles is characterised by feel-good words that have little real meaning. Who, for instance, is to determine what the duties of stewardship are that we have apparently received from our Creator? Prince Charles? The large corporations who seek to profit from the poor or the poor themselves whose very attempt at a better life for them and their families e.g. in obtaining refrigeration at an affordable cost. Are the poor not entitled to advance themselves, even at the expense of a minor increase in fossil fuel demand.

It would be helpful if Prince Charles could define his terms and specify exactly what the ancient or heart-felt wisdom is that he wishes us to follow. He has benefited directly from science in everything that he does and owns and perhaps he might ask himself a number of questions:

- Should the poor be denied resources because he or others have enough?
- Is he following his own advice in his own life?
- Is the fight against disease, which is a part of nature, to be discontinued?
- Can he point to a single event in the history of his family that he can prove was caused by the Creator?

The organisers of the lectures might ask themselves:

- What particular benefit does Prince Charles bring to the debate other than celebrity from an accident of birth?
- Why did you allow a contribution to go unchallenged? Are the Prince's future subjects unworthy of debating with him?

Edward Armstrong, UK

I was so pleased to hear Prince Charles speaking out against the 'techno' society we live in today. I agree very strongly that we are going down the wrong path. We become less and less attached to nature and abuse our environment so much. It amazes me how arrogant and short-sighted human beings are. Do we really think that this world is solely for our use? I have had strong environmental feelings since I was a teenager and over the years the warning signs have become more and more apparent.

Scientists at first quaffed at the idea of a hole in the ozone layer, now we have more than one and it is an accepted fact – skin cancer rates are rising. I can remember when global warming was supposed to be scaremongering by the 'hair-brained' environmentalists, as well! As a member of a number of environmental groups, I'm afraid I do agree when they take 'direct action' against polluters and multinational companies who manipulate governments to increase profits with no consideration for people at all – apart from their shareholders of course!

If Prince Charles happens to read this – 'Please Sir, when you visit the Island in July 2000, to celebrate our ancient government, please could you whisper in some of the MHK's ears that we don't want an incinerator to solve our refuse problems and pollute our air with dioxins and increase CO_2, when the world is supposed to be reducing emissions – we want to encourage re-cycling, not waste resourses. The IOM Friends of the earth group don't want the 'techno' fix at a huge initial outlay and a maintenance cost that will cripple the ratepayers. A recycling scheme would be a fraction of the cost of building and maintaining an incinerator and it would put something useful back into the community (composting, valuable materials; aluminium, glass).

I apologise for keeping the comments so 'local', but it just shows how governments go for the quick and easy 'fix' – which in the long run backfires, be it in the public's health or in escalating costs. But of course, most of the politicians have moved on by then!

Phil Corlett, Isle of Man

Not one word about excessive population. There is and never has been an agricultural (farming) community that has lived in harmony with nature. History has been a continuous serious of ecological collapses as humans have, without the excuse of 'globalisation', over-exploited and destroyed their habitats. The left will never be taken seriously (nor should they be) until they address these biological realities and develop an analysis with more depth than poor=good, rich=evil.

Dean, USA

How can you summarise this debate without once mentioning population control? It is a complete waste of money and resources to air this debate without hitting the heart of the environmental issue by talking about how we are going to stop raping the earth by encouraging more children? I had honestly thought that you were actually going to build up the courage to tackle the true issue behind conservation and the environment. These speakers have no interest in saving the planet ... just saving the human race. All I have heard is the rights of the poor, and of the sick. What about the rights of the animals and plants that were here well before we were?

This is the selfish attitude we have to get rid off. None of this waffle about the 'language we are using'. Please wake up and realise that talk is not what is needed but solid action to prevent the human race destroying something that is amazingly beautiful ... life itself!

Steve Lee, UK

Science speaks the truth and nothing but the truth, but nowhere near the whole truth. Prince Charles's critique stressed spiritual values, but science itself can also be expanded to include wider values. The trouble is that the science that creates and underpins a new technology like genetic engineering is inappropriate and insufficient as a discipline to determine how and whether it could or should be applied. It requires another science to understand the ecology and relationships between human society and natural processes and how the new technology would influence these.

So, while scientists have already criticised the Prince for not understanding the science, there is no reason to suppose that molecular biologists understand the science of the human ecology of application. It is outside their field and about other subject areas. I hope that the Fellows of the Royal Society can take up the challenge implied by Prince Charles's lecture, and promote the more encompassing science that is now needed.

Dr Ulrich Loening, Centre for Human Ecology, Scotland, UK